Good Medicine

Four Las Vegas Doctors and the Golden Age of Medicine

Good Medicine

Four Las Vegas Doctors and the Golden Age of Medicine

Annie Blachley

Greasewood Press 🌿 Reno

GREASEWOOD PRESS
Pathology/350 Reno, Nevada 89557

FIRST PRINTING
1 2 3 4 5 6 7 8 9

Production of *Good Medicine: Four Las Vegas Doctors
and the Golden Age of Medicine* was made possible by a grant
from The Great Basin History of Medicine Program
of the Department of Pathology, University of Nevada School
of Medicine and the John Ben Snow Foundation.
This title is the first in a series on The Golden Age of
Medicine in Nevada.

Text and jacket design by Carrie Nelson House

Library of Congress Catalog Card Number and CIP data are
located at end of book.

Dr. Gerald Joseph Sylvain passed away in Las Vegas on December 30, 1999 at the age of 90. He will long be remembered as the small-town country doctor with the heart as big as Nevada.

For Peter and Jessica, who have always believed in me.

Contents

Part 1: Gerald Joseph Sylvain, M.D.

Part 2: Joseph Matthias George, Jr., M.D.

Part 3: James Daniel Barger, M.D.

Part 4: Leonard Kreisler, M.D.

Illustrations

Lieutenant Dorothy Marie O'Donnell, R.N., U.S. Army Nurse
Corps, 1945.
Joseph M. George, Jr., M.D. and Drs. Theodore Jacobs, Kirk
Cammack, and Hugh Follmer, 1966.
Dr. Joseph M. George, Jr. and family, May, 1993.

following page 120

Part 3: James Daniel Barger, M.D.
Young Jim Barger, circa 1918.
Undergraduate Jim Barger at the University of North Dakota, 1938.
James Daniel Barger cavorts with his future wife, Janie Ray Regan,
1939.
Las Vegas' Sunrise Hospital, the early 1960s.
A bearded Dr. James Barger, Bolivia, 1945.
Dr. James Barger and his wife, Janie Regan Barger, 1981.
Dr. James Barger enjoying retirement, 1998.

Part 4: Leonard Kreisler, M.D.
Clark County Indigent Hospital, 1931.
Young Len Kreisler with his family, circa 1933.
Dr. Leonard Kreisler and his bride, Joan, 1957.
University Medical Center of Southern Nevada, 1976.
Dr. Leonard Kreisler, Captain, U.S. Army Medical Corps, the
late 1950s.
Dr. Leonard Kreisler, medical school graduation, 1957.
University Medical Center of Southern Nevada Chief of Staff
Leonard Kreisler, M.D., 1982.
Participating physician Leonard Kreisler, M.D., U.S. Olympic
Training Center, 1982.
A happily retired Dr. Leonard Kreisler dons his beloved cowboy
hat, 1998.

Acknowledgments

As the first book I have written, this publication represents a milestone in my life, one that could not have been achieved without the help and inspiration of many people. Without the encouragement of my parents, Ralph and Evelyn Wilkinson, and the pep talks from my sister, Mary McCarthy, and my daughter, Erika Hoernle, I would never have set pen to paper. The people at Dr. Robert L. Buckingham's office in Ojai, California—Dr. B., Tracy, Peggy, Marie, and Shannon—who still practice good medicine and listen to the patients, gave me medical knowledge and friendship.

This book began with writer Kay Fahey, one of the founders of the Unnamed Writers Group of Reno who recommended me for the project. I am also most grateful to Anton P. Sohn, M.D., founder and chief historian of University of Nevada Great Basin History of Medicine Program and Pathology Department chair at the University of Nevada, Reno, for offering erudite guidance and demonstrating endless patience. Dr. Sohn's staff at the University, Lynda Mulvey and Theresa Garrison, cheerfully provided their much-needed, capable assistance. Both Dr. Sohn and Lisa Puleo, Executive Director of Clark County Medical Society in Las Vegas, gave me the foundation of these stories through their oral history interviews, along with vital historical information. At the University of Nevada, Reno, Mike Sion, editor of *Silver & Blue* and nonfiction book author, gave his practical advice and encouragement. Jeremy Murray, Lab Manager at the College of Education Computer Lab at University of Nevada, Reno, helped me salvage my manuscript—with patience and grace—after my beloved but ancient computer passed on to cyber heaven. Publicist Laurie Haley at the University of Nevada

School of Medicine in Las Vegas and the staff of the Nevada Historical Society and Nevada State Medical Association provided important background details.

I could not have completed this book without the patient, dogged, and intelligent resourcefulness of reference librarians Ian and Sharon Campbell, Anne Hawkins, Larry Hillman, Barbara Kaufman, Marilyn Matylinsky, and Marc Tiar at the downtown Reno (main) branch of the Washoe County Library; I'll choose a librarian over the Internet any day for the fastest, most accurate research. I also thank Drs. Ronald Slaughter and Gerald R. Sylvain, Dr. Gerald Joseph Sylvain's son, for their valuable insights.

Finally, I offer my gratitude to the subjects of this book—Drs. Gerald Joseph Sylvain, Joseph Matthias George, Jr., Dorothy George, R.N., James Daniel Barger, M.D., and Leonard Kreisler—for their hospitality and openness in sharing their memories, and for telling it like it was.

Preface

This book tells the stories of four doctors who practiced medicine in the Las Vegas of a more innocent time. Like many who settled the West, none were natives of Nevada. Hailing from the midwest or the East Coast, they struck out on their own to practice their skills as healers of humanity from the 1940s through the 1980s. One doctor encountered bizarre folk remedies for life-threatening illnesses; others battled with infections before the invention of sulfa drugs or antibiotics; one achieved greatness—in politics as well as in medicine—without clamoring for recognition; another, looking after atomic test site workers during the Cold War, came up against intolerance and racial prejudice. Despite their different experiences, all four share the same belief: the era during which they practiced medicine in Las Vegas was the golden age of medicine.

In telling their stories, I have taken a departure from the traditional oral history format, in which the subject's remembrances are recorded, transcribed, organized, and published. To improve clarity—and to capture the essence of each subject for an interesting read—I have enhanced the narrative, creating biographical profiles. The subjects' words appear exactly as recorded, with little or no editing, whenever possible. The accounts are based on oral history interviews conducted between 1994 and 1998 by the interviewers credited below. In 1998 and 1999, I conducted additional interviews based on the original transcripts.

The stories are told in chronological order in four parts. In Part One, Gerald Joseph Sylvain, M.D., remembers his years as a general practitioner in Las Vegas beginning in 1942, when World War II was in full swing. Now ninety years old and retired, Dr. Sylvain is the last survivor of the six physician-owners of the Las Vegas Hospital and Clinic, the city's first hospital. His interview was conducted by Anton P. Sohn, M.D., chairman of the pathology department at the University of Nevada School of Medicine, founder and chief historian of the medical school's Great Basin History of Medicine division, and author of several volumes on the history of medicine.

Part Two details the life of Joseph Matthias George, Jr., M.D., who came to Las Vegas in 1946, four years after Dr. Sylvain. There were just thirteen doctors and two hospitals in the city when Dr. George, assisted by his wife, registered nurse Dorothy George, started practicing there. This sole practitioner delivered at least 6,000 local babies, cared for those children who grew up to start families of their own, then delivered their babies, and so on, until his retirement in 1988 at age seventy-five. The interviews with Dr. George and with Dorothy George, R.N. were conducted by Lisa Puleo, executive director of Las Vegas' Clark County Medical Society, who was instrumental in gathering information, interviewing, and transcribing much of the material used in this section as well as throughout this book.

In Part Three, James D. Barger, M.D. reveals how he worked to improve the quality of a young medical community as it entered the modern world of technology and specialization. Now eighty-two years old, Dr. Barger came to Las Vegas in 1964 as one of the first pathologists in the city; the pathology group he founded still consults exclusively with Sunrise Hospital. Working behind the scenes in national politics through 1989, he helped to bring the Federal government and local laboratories together for a common goal: quality control. Dr. Barger was interviewed by Lisa Puleo.

Leonard Kreisler, M.D., the subject of Part Four, describes how he left his old-fashioned country practice in upstate New York to discover the wild West in 1973. As medical director for the U.S. Department of Energy's Nevada Test Site for nearly twenty years, Dr. Kreisler became a specialist in occupational medicine for the atomic age. He was also one of the prime movers behind Southern Nevada Memorial Hospital's name being changed to University Medical Center of Southern Nevada, and spearheaded the establishment of the Hospital foundation and the Children's Miracle Network Telethon. Lisa Puleo conducted the interview with Dr. Kreisler.

The final section—Speaking Frankly: Las Vegas Health Professionals on Managed Care and Other Challenges to Modern Medicine—brings the physicians together for an informal, albeit no holds barred forum. Along with several other Las Vegas medical professionals, one retired and one still in practice, these doctors offer their astute, well-educated observations—and their gut feelings—on the subjects they know best. Asking and answering hard questions, they try to bring about a favorable prognosis for a patient in trouble: modern medical practice. What went awry to change the practice of medicine so radically? Can its lifeblood be revived? Why does the golden age of medicine still engender such nostalgia from those who lived it—and such admiration from those too young to remember it? These experienced professionals' talents as examiners, diagnosticians, and healers—and honest humanitarians—shine in this section.

It is my hope that all those who concern themselves with medicine will draw inspiration and guidance from the well-honed skills, wisdom, and kindnesses these medical pioneers have been generous enough to share.

Good Medicine

Four Las Vegas Doctors and the Golden Age of Medicine

Introduction
Before the Glitz: The Golden Age
of Medicine in Las Vegas

There is a desert-hued city nestled in a southern Nevada valley that is like no other city on earth. Hordes of the curious from all over the world flock to this Mecca of commerce to marvel at its mega-resorts, stare at its star-studded Strip, and gawk at its gambling castles. At once both elegant and tawdry, most of it is over the top, including its population: a million plus in 1999, and still exploding.

But few may realize that this paved paradise was originally a simple area of grassland fed by springs, the home of the Native American Paiute tribe. Later named Las Vegas (Spanish for the meadows or plains), it became a stopping place on the Old Spanish Trail from Santa Fe to California. By the 1850s, it consisted of several small villages populated by Mormon settlers from the valley of the Great Salt Lake and a mining camp full of down-on-their-luck prospectors. Disdained as the unsightly outback of the poorest state, the arid Mojave Desert province of Clark County was not even attached to the state until two years after Nevada's 1864 admission to the Union. By the turn of the century, there were thirty residents.

The city was founded in 1905 when the San Pedro, Los Angeles, and Salt Lake Railroad auctioned off townsites in what would become the core of downtown. But the desert outpost—actually a railroad siding, a few stores, a wood-framed tent hotel, and a railroad tent hospital—languished, mostly forgotten. The frontier was catapulted into worldwide prominence in 1931, when the legalization and taxing of gambling in Nevada along with the start of construction on Boulder (now Hoover) Dam created a bonanza of jobs, unlimited water, and cheap hydroelectric power. The same year, the city gained notoriety when the legislature amended Nevada's divorce laws to require a mere six-week residency.

I

Yet everyday life for most Las Vegans—and the doctors who cared for them—was not that different from life across America. When people went to the doctor, they usually paid cash on the spot—before the lure of credit cards, before the health insurance industry began clamoring for their piece of the pie, and before Medicare and Medicaid. In 1940, when Las Vegas had only 8,422 residents (Reno, its mighty neighbor to the north, boasted 21,317), few people had insurance—so there was no need for time-consuming, expensive billing and collection procedures. With no malpractice insurance for doctors, there were fewer lawyers than today. Perhaps people did not sue others—especially doctors—so readily. Perhaps people were less greedy.

This book tells the stories of four Las Vegas medical pioneers during that simpler time: general practitioners Gerald Joseph Sylvain and Joseph Matthias George, Jr., pathologist James D. Barger, and occupational medicine specialist Leonard P. Kreisler. Looking back on their experiences with the gift of hindsight, all four revere the years between the 1940s and the 1980s as the golden age of medicine. It was an age during which they found the freedom to shape their destinies and build up personal fortunes—not through games of chance, not by amassing vast sums of wealth or through insatiable brokering and deal-making, but because they were living examples of old-fashioned hard work, ethics, and integrity, with some pluck thrown in for good measure. The fortune each discovered was realized in the joys they found in practicing the healing art.

The candid insights revealed in the recollections of these medical men debunk the popular perception that most doctors are wealthy, ruthless business people whose days revolve around playing golf or lazing around their estates. Though they devoted decades to their calling, their purpose was not to get rich—or "to get Vegasized," as one of the doctors interviewed dubs the seductive quest for wealth that ensnares some residents. These dedicated physicians just wanted to make a difference and to raise the standard of health care in their community. Las Vegas is all the healthier for their having made their mark there.

On a larger scale, their remembrances of a once-naive town, full of outlandish characters and just plain folks, reflect how uncomplicated America was—before it started hurtling headlong into the twentieth century. Those halcyon years shine in sharp contrast to the current state of life and of medicine, illustrating the vast difference between then and now.

The truth today is that despite huge advances in research and technology, many physicians are finding themselves at crossroads in their careers. Simply put, doctors have less and less time to care for patients, and for many, their economic survival is in jeopardy. Constantly cutting inroads into their day—and their income—are the ever-escalating legal costs, malpractice insurance premiums, high overhead, an avalanche of paperwork, the government's reduction of fees, and the restrictive policies of insurance companies and managed care organizations.

Because physicians are perceived—often erroneously—as having what lawyers call "deep pockets," or abundant malpractice insurance coverage, they are often targeted in our litigious society. The question of innocence is meaningless when physicians must fork over exorbitant amounts to keep a frivolous suit from going to court. And the malpractice insurance carriers extol a healthy chunk of income, even when a doctor's career is exemplary and suit-free; high insurance premiums must be paid, in case the doctor is sued in the future.

Also eroding a doctor's income is office overhead. Back in the golden era of medicine, before wonder drugs and sophisticated diagnostic equipment became commonplace, a doctor typically had rather modest expenses: a small office, one nurse who often doubled as a receptionist, and a modicum of supplies. Today, a physician's earnings can be eaten up by ever-rising salaries and benefits for an appointment secretary; for two assistants to handle insurance billing, paperwork, and questions from patients and insurance companies; and for a nurse. Then there is the outside billing service; advertising; marketing; computer consultants; lawyers; bookkeepers; accountants; collection agencies; subscriptions; memberships; licenses; rent in a favorable location; parking space fees (for employees and patients); medical supplies; uniforms; office supplies; a state-of-the-art communications array (computers, office phones, cell phones, pagers, fax machines, and an answering service); laboratory equipment and supplies; furnishings; repairs; cleaning; maintenance; and more. In addition, doctors are expected to donate to every national and local association and/or charity imaginable.

Modern practitioners and their employees are finding that their time is increasingly taken up with countless authorization and approval documents. A former medical secretary to a general practitioner hit the nail on the head when she resigned, stating she was fed up with practicing for that great paper-shuffling race in the sky. Still another pointed observation comes from an internist's nurse, who says that the incessant paperwork is what keeps the "JJs"—the "job justifiers"—happy.

But it is the single phenomenon of managed care—some call it mismanaged care—which has probably brought the greatest pressure to bear on modern healers. Managed care takes many forms, including HMOs (health management organizations) and PPOs (preferred provider organizations). In the managed care network, a family practitioner or internist agrees to serve as the patient's main doctor. That doctor is designated as the primary care physician; this participating (or preferred) provider is sometimes called the gatekeeper physician. The doctor provides care for a reduced cost to the insurance company and the patient, and the company refers patients in the network to the doctor. The main doctor is encouraged to handle virtually all the patient's needs and to not recommend specialists, to hold costs down. The patient pays a monthly premium to the insurance company plus a flat fee (called a co-payment or co-pay) for each visit to the doctor.

In theory, managed care is supposed to provide the patient with care at a reduced cost, while making up the reduced payments to the doctor with more patient referrals. In reality, the doctor often ends sacrificing income, receiving only a monthly pittance from the insurance company in exchange for providing unlimited monthly visits to the patient.

And what happens when a patient requires an appointment with a specialist—i.e. an oncologist (tumor specialist)—to treat a malignant growth? What occurs if the very best specialist the gatekeeper physician recommends is not a participating provider? First, the main doctor (the gatekeeper) must be seen to fill out paperwork referring the patient. The patient must then wait to see the specialist until the insurance company processes the paperwork, which can sometimes take weeks. Problems arise because it is not always physicians who evaluate medical necessity: oftentimes it is registered nurses or insurance company staffers, who are not always medically qualified to evaluate a case. They dictate just how a patient will—or will not—be treated. That sometimes means that the recommended treatment will be refused, especially if it is costly. This manipulation of the concept of what is medically necessary often ties the hands of both physicians and patients. In addition, if a gatekeeper physician or specialist is not contracted with the managed care insurance company, the patient's freedom to choose the doctor is compromised.

The system has given itself the last word on every question of patient care—the who, what, when, where, how, and how much. Managed care decides who will care for patients; what will be done for them; when, where, and how they will treated; and how much doctors can charge. Many managed care organizations have lost sight of the fact that they were created to help health care providers care for people. But the bottom line of most modern HMOs and PPOs is to minimize cost and make money. The result: patient care often ends up at the bottom of the list.

These issues have been building in California and many other states since the 1980s, and in recent years have escalated in Nevada. Dealing with the ethical and financial obstacles—from managed care, increased expenses, legal hindrances, and government bureaucracy—make it seem nearly impossible for doctors to practice good medicine and care for people.

The current state of medicine may make many yearn for a return to some semblance of the fairness, good will, and open communication that were the hallmark of the golden era of medicine—when doctors were free to do their utmost to heal their patients as they were trained to do, become the best doctors they could be, and practice good medicine.

1

Gerald Joseph Sylvain, M.D.

General Practitioner; Years Practiced: 1934–1994

I spend quite a lot of time with my

patients. I don't run them in like

it's a factory and run 'em out. I spend

a lot of time with them.

> —*Gerald Joseph Sylvain, M.D.*

Hard Times, Hard Work, and Croquette

1909–1926

Gerald Joseph Sylvain, M.D. has been a lucky man. But unlike most people who come to Nevada seeking good fortune, his success stemmed not from games of chance but from hard work, ambition, and foresight. When he left Goldfield, Nevada and took a gamble on Las Vegas in 1942, he found a young, innocent city, a place he would call home for nearly six decades. The people of that small city, in turn, welcomed him as their treasure. His gamble paid off: with sixty years of practice as a Nevada physician, he holds the number two state record for the most years in practice, just behind his longtime friend, Dr. Noah Smernoff of Reno.

Sylvain worked as a general practitioner during that golden era when the playing field of medicine was drastically different. To begin with, in 1934, when he started practice in Nevada, doctors routinely made house calls. By 1945, when the annual income of most southern Nevada physicians was around $10,000, office visits cost half a sawbuck, or under $5—a striking contrast to fees in the late 1990s, when a typical office visit runs $85. Malpractice insurance was unheard of, there was very little health insurance, and Medicare did not exist. Most patients paid in cash before the advent of credit or charge accounts.

But beyond the finances—and equally or more important—were the prevailing attitudes of the day. It was a time when a doctor had the freedom to focus on the one thing that mattered above all else: patient care. Dr. Sylvain explains his approach simply but eloquently when he says, "I enjoyed the practice immensely in those days. We had patients that we became very friendly with. We really looked after them."

When Sylvain first came to that simpler Las Vegas in March of 1942, the city was still considered a dusty, albeit growing, desert town—but it had 10,000 people. The young doctor's home town of Butte, Montana and idyllic upbringing must have seemed as though they were halfway around the world. The product of a large, close-knit, French-Canadian family, Sylvain had been raised to be as ruggedly self-reliant and ambitious as his forbears. He would need that solid preparation—plus a strong sense of humor and sheer will power—to get him through medical school in record time, to earn the distinction of being the first one in his family to graduate from college, and to go on to a sixty-year career as a beloved family doctor. Deciding on a medical career also meant leaving his close family ties and saying goodbye to his beloved home town. But with his sights set on the golden opportunities to be found outside Butte, he made his choice and said his farewells to friends and family—in much the same way as his grandfather had done years earlier when emigrating to America.

In the late 1800s, Sylvain's grandfather, Felix Sylvain, worked as a lumberjack in an area of Canada. But hard economic times befell Felix, his wife, and their eight sons and daughters. Felix chose to heed his gut instincts: bidding adieu to Quebec, he and his family moved to Butte, Montana to try to carve out a better life.

One of the Sylvain children was little Arthur, who was very young when his family set foot on American soil. But even in their newfound land of opportunity, times were so tough that young Arthur had to drop out of school in the fourth grade, to go to work to help support the family. Young Arthur worked hard and put in long hours at Paumei's Dye House, a cleaning and dye works in Butte, with his brother, Pete. But the Sylvain brothers took the skills learned at the plant and went on to build on that knowledge. They turned their tough times around, not by borrowing heavily from a bank, but through old-fashioned, nose-to-the-grindstone work, and like so many other immigrant families, they were able to taste the American dream by opening up their own business. They established City Cleaning and Dye Works on Broadway in Butte, and kept it up and running for many years.

Along the way, Arthur met and married Florida, also of French-Canadian descent, who had been brought to Butte as an infant by her parents. They started a family, and on January 23, 1909, their second son, Gerald, was born in Butte. They strived to keep their French-Canadian heritage alive, and whenever Gerald's paternal grandmother would visit she would speak to Gerald and his brothers only in French, in hopes that they would pick up the language; as a result, Gerald did learn to speak some French.

While Gerald's father Arthur Sylvain had to work hard to keep his business running and support his family, he still valued simple pleasures and time with his family. Arthur Sylvain was not the type to take on debt by gallivanting about the globe in search of the biggest and best with itinerary-heavy expensive vacations. Instead, the Sylvain clan spent their time—not their money—on pastimes such as frequent junkets to the many beautiful rivers not far from town. For young Gerald and his two brothers, childhood was an idyllic blend of years spent exploring the outdoors and sharing good times.

"We were a very close family," recalls Sylvain. "There were very many family outings. When not working in the plant my father loved to fish. Every time he had any time off he'd go fishing. When we took a two weeks' vacation, we'd load the tent and all the paraphernalia in the car and then we'd camp somewhere along a river."

Gerald grew up in the pre-electronic era, before the dawn of television and its stranglehold over youth. Instead, he remembers many family doings at his grandparents' place, with lots of outdoor recreation everyone in the family could enjoy. He recalls also that an uncle who lived down on the flats in Butte had a lighted croquette court in his back yard. Among Sylvain's fondest memories are the balmy summer evenings the family spent playing croquette. As the women and young girls moved gracefully across the green in their long dresses, the happy sounds of children's laughter echoed through the night, punctuated by the sharp click of wooden mallets striking wooden balls.

All through grade school, Gerald Sylvain was a good student and a very good speller. After his eighth grade graduation, he attended his first year of high school in Helena, Montana at Mount St. Charles College, later renamed Carroll College, then transferred to Central Catholic High School in Butte. When not in school, he worked in his father's plant. Sylvain was good at math and chemistry, as was his lab partner and friend, William Ruckward; the two decided they wanted to enroll at Montana State College in Bozeman, Montana.

But a chance visit to the dentist's office radically altered Sylvain's career path. After looking through a Marquette University yearbook his dentist had let him take home to study, Sylvain suddenly changed his mind. To this day, he can't explain why.

"I read all about it and I said to Bill Ruckward, my pal, 'You know, I'm going to go to Marquette University and I don't think I'll take up engineering. I think I'm going to be a doctor.'"

Ruckward decided he would go to Marquette also, as an engineering major. The two said goodbye to Butte and headed for Milwaukee, Wisconsin and Marquette University. In 1926, Ruckward enrolled in engineering at the Jesuit school; Sylvain enrolled in pre-med.

Medical School in Record Time and Bathtub Gin

1926–1934

Because of Sylvain's excellent high school math and chemistry courses, he was able to tutor students at Marquette. It soon became obvious that his career switch from engineering to medicine had been the right one: his grades were so good that after only two years in premed, he was admitted to Marquette's medical school. But his tutoring requirements combined with his own study load proved to be a strain.

"Most of the students in my class had four years of college and it was kind of difficult for me. I had my hands full just trying to keep up," Sylvain remembers. One way he would unwind from the pressure was by continuing the sport he had taken up in high school with his pal Bill Ruckward. At Marquette, they played on the same hockey team as three superb Canadian players, McKenzie, MacTear, and McFadden. Sylvain is still fiercely proud of that team.

"We probably had the best hockey team in the country at that time, 1926, '27, and '28. Before then, hockey was considered a minor sport, and awarded by a sweater with a little 'm.' Because we had such a successful season, the university made hockey a major sport and we got the big 'M' and became members of the 'M' Club. With the little 'm,' one couldn't become a member of the 'M' Club. I am still a member of the 'M' Club."

The Roaring Twenties were in full swing when Sylvain moved into a social fraternity house on a corner of Wisconsin Avenue near the school. Alpha Gamma Phi, which sponsored athletes, was so noisy that when exam time came, Sylvain had to rent a room away from the fraternity house for a couple of weeks with his roommate, Gregory Grimaldi, so they wouldn't be disturbed while studying for exams.

In anatomy class at the old medical school at Fourth and Reservoir in

Milwaukee, Sylvain and forty-three other students would work in teams of four; two would dissect the lower half of cadavers and two the upper half, and then they'd switch. The cadavers on the table were re-embalmed to keep them from rotting, and when the students left at night they'd pull a damp formaldehyde sheet over them, then come back and work on them the next day, recalls Sylvain.

Summers offered little time for relaxing. Sylvain would return home and work in the family cleaning business; one summer, he also sold newspapers before going to work. Medical school was expensive, but Gerald was able to attend because his father had been in business for awhile and had saved up money.

"My dad financed me all the way through school. I was not extravagant and dad always helped. If I needed money, I just wrote a letter and he'd send me a check. Not only that, he bought a new Cadillac the year he sent me to school (in 1926). It cost $4,000 and weighed four thousand pounds, so he paid a dollar a pound," Sylvain remembers. With a big laugh he adds, "But think of the cost: $4,000!"

During the last year of school, things back in Butte got a little tough, so Sylvain got a job as a night doctor at the A.O. Smith Corporation in Milwaukee. He was paid $125 a month, which was good pay in those days, he recalls. He got the job by joining Phi Chi, a medical fraternity which passed the position from one member to another. But he had to make some sacrifices: because the job started in July, he didn't get to spend that summer at home. The position required a car, so he had to come up with $235 for a used Model A Ford. But that car got him through his senior year of medical school, his internship, and his first year in private practice, when he sold it for $235.

Another purchase Sylvain made while in medical school proved to be an even better investment: the microscope he bought for his bacteriology course. He would use it in practice for the next sixty years to look at wet smears (cells which have been smeared or spread onto a glass slide and stained for examination under a microscope; includes vaginal swabs for organisms).

After two years of college and two of medical school, Sylvain got his bachelor of science degree; he earned his M.D. then did a rotating internship at Milwaukee County Hospital from 1932 to 1933. Just twenty-four years old during the speakeasy days, he and his friends would experiment and make bathtub gin from alcohol and juniper berries. Sometimes they'd head into downtown Milwaukee to places like the Schroeder Hotel to listen to big-name orchestras. Dances like the jitterbug or the Lindy Hop, named after Charles Lindbergh's epic 1927 flight, were all the rage. Hotels couldn't serve alcohol, but they could serve the mix, Sylvain says, so the interns brought their own whiskey or other hard liquor and hid it under a napkin.

"We'd mix a drink and get fortified so as to have enough guts to get up and dance," Sylvain remembers. "It was fun going to school at Marquette University during the speakeasy days. If we wanted to go into a speakeasy, we knocked on the door and somebody would look through a little opening and see who you were. They might let you in, and they might not. Those were the Al Capone days in Chicago."

Sylvain roomed again with Gregory Grimaldi. As interns, they were paid $25 a month plus room and board. Sylvain says that was enough to buy cigarettes at 99¢ a carton, with enough money left over for some odds and ends. The County Hospital was an excellent place to do an internship, says Sylvain, because it was packed full during those depression years. He did minor surgery and assisted on many cases, but was unable to perform major surgery alone because a residency was required, and not easy to get. He also delivered babies—lots of them.

"We were so full in the obstetrical department that we delivered some of the babies in the hall. I probably delivered at least forty babies in my six-week rotation," recalls Sylvain.

Sylvain completed his internship in 1933, and, diploma in hand, went home for six months to think about what he wanted to do. Although he was the first in his family to graduate from college, that accomplishment did not earn any extra points in the industrious Sylvain household. He supposes, he says with a chuckle, that his parents were proud of him, but they didn't tell him so.

The Great Depression dragged on, paralyzing the American economy. And even though a Saturday matinee cost a mere nickel, including two movies, a serial, cartoons, and the newsreels, jobs were few and far between. Then Sylvain heard about an opening in Goldfield, Nevada, just east of Bishop in northeastern California. He realized that taking that job would mean leaving his home town and family, but, as he explains, "It was during the depression, and money was kind of scarce. The idea was to get somewhere where they'd put up a little money." Wasting no time, he went to talk with Dr. J. L. McCarthy, a local doctor in Butte who had practiced years earlier in Goldfield. After their talk, Sylvain accepted the position. He would be taking over the practice of Dr. Jack C. Cherry, who would be relocating to Tonopah, Nevada in 1933. Dr. Cherry had come down to Goldfield from the railroad hospital in

Glendive, Montana in 1924. Sylvain says Dr. Cherry was instrumental in getting him to come to Goldfield; he would reappear in Sylvain's life often over the years.

Sylvain would be furnished with an office and paid $100 a month to look after the gold miners of Goldfield, and he could start a private practice. On January 23, 1934, young Dr. Sylvain left Butte during a blinding snowstorm and drove for two days to Goldfield.

Pneumonia, Pigeon Poultices, and Public Health

1934–1940

GOLDFIELD, NEVADA

ANN ARBOR, MICHIGAN

As soon as Sylvain reached Goldfield, he got his Nevada medical license, which he got by reciprocity as a result of being licensed in Wisconsin. Young, enthusiastic, and fresh out of medical school, the new small-town family doctor eagerly anticipated seeing his first patient. But it would take a bit of time for people to get over their skepticism of the new kid in town, who was, after all, just twenty-five years old. Even if he was a qualified licensed physician, there was no getting around his age and inexperience.

Sylvain still gets a tremendous kick out of talking about his first days in practice. As he tells it, when he went to his office at 8:00 A.M. the first morning, there were no patients. He went to the office on the second day and there were still no patients. On the third day, there was actually somebody in the waiting room. Sylvain thought, "Oh my goodness, I'm going to have my first patient. I was so happy. Well, come to find out, he was a book salesman—and not my first patient after all."

As Sylvain describes it, the town of Goldfield wasn't much in 1934. At one time the biggest city in Nevada with 22,000 people, Goldfield had produced eighty million dollars' worth of precious metals, including "the yellow metal," during Nevada's twentieth century mining boom in the years between 1903 and 1920. But the ensuing years saw the town plagued by flood, fire, and the fluctuations of its mining boom-and-bust economy.

When Sylvain arrived, the population consisted of five hundred people, a butcher shop, a few bars, a service station, a boarding house on Fifth Street, and not much else. To go shopping, take in a movie, or to get to the closest hospital, people would zip over to the bigger town of

Tonopah, twenty-six miles away. In those days it didn't take long, explains Sylvain, because there were no speed limits.

Goldfield's chief distinction came from the invention of the first adjustable head for a golf stick. To Sylvain, such an invention was unusual out in the middle of a desert, where there was no golf course. The all-in-one club had been developed when Goldfield Catholic priest Father Gavin laid out a golf course on the dry lake at Joe Justi's Alkali Spring. Because a ball would go for miles on the hard surface of that long course, packing a set of clubs became tiresome. Father Gavin and Dr. Jack Cherry came up with a club with an adjustable head that could be used as a driver, niblic, mashie, and putter. They got Edward Lembke, secretary of Goldfield Deep Mines, to set up a factory in California, and a golf pro named Navak sponsored the clubs. But after production and marketing problems, the unsold Navakclubs ended up being stored by Dr. Cherry in Goldfield.

Because Sylvain was a single gentleman when he came to Goldfield, he lodged in a boarding house. His room had its own little coal stove while most of the other rooms didn't have their own stoves, because, he says, the new doctor in town was special. He was quickly educated about boarding house living one evening after dinner when he sat socializing with the other boarders and some visiting schoolteachers. He kept waiting for them to get up and leave so he could get some rest and have a bath.

"When nobody made any move to go, I decided I'd get up. Well, they were so relieved when I got up," Sylvain remembers. "They were waiting for me so they could take the hot water off the coal stove. They were going to help pour hot water in the tub so that I could have a bath!"

His office, upstairs in the Elks Club Building, consisted of a waiting room, another room with a desk and examining table, and a steam sterilizer. At first, there was a pharmacy but no pharmacist, so when he wrote a prescription, he had to rush through the back door of the pharmacy to dispense pills. He would see a patient and then if he wasn't busy, he'd run over to the Elks Lodge, also upstairs, where he learned to play poker, whist, gin rummy, and cribbage. Downstairs were a post office and a barber shop; he recalls that the barber, J.J. Noone, doubled as the town mortician. With a laugh, Sylvain adds, "I'm not so sure that he didn't become sheriff for a short time."

Patients started trickling in after a time, yet he was never very busy, he remembers, seeing fifteen patients a day at most. His time was spent doing some fracture work, delivering babies, and taking care of kids. Being in general practice in Goldfield was not all that different than it would have been in Butte, says Sylvain. Despite the fact that Nevada was still regarded by some as the wild, rip-roarin' frontier, there were not an abnormal number of tobacco- or alcohol-related cases, he recalls.

Many of his patients were pregnant women who would come to the office for prenatal care. He would deliver the babies in their homes, then go back and see the mother and baby for ten days. The total charge, including the delivery: $50.

"I had a medical bag with my obstetrical instruments and medicine. If I had to have some help, I usually used the husband. And, once in awhile, I'd use a chloroform drip for anesthesia. They were all pretty much natural births with a little bit of chloroform," Sylvain recalls, adding to reflect, "It's kind of scary when I think about it now."

Though Sylvain did not have many surgical emergencies in Goldfield, he did have one patient with a ruptured tubal pregnancy. Making the diagnosis on the basis of a history of missed periods, sudden onset, and a rigid and sore belly, he recalls, "She wasn't bleeding real heavy, so I sent her to California for surgery, and everything came out all right."

Because there were no hospitals in Goldfield, patients requiring hospitalization would go to one of Tonopah's two hospitals, the County Hospital or the Mines Hospital; each had a whopping ten beds. At that time Tonopah had two doctors besides Dr. Cherry: Dr. John Clement Cowden and Dr. Robert Craig. The Mines Hospital was operated by Dr. Craig, who did abdominal surgery and as a rule only operated in Tonopah. Dr. Craig later bought into a medical building and moved to Reno, but then retired from practice, as far as Sylvain knows. Dr. Cherry also did some surgery.

In 1934, before the advent of sulfa drugs or antibiotics, pneumonia was a big problem in Goldfield. Sylvain admits that as an intern, he had gotten conflicting advice on how to treat the disease. "A hotshot attending doctor would make rounds and he'd say, 'Open up all these windows so these patients can breathe.'" Then Sylvain would make rounds with another hotshot who would say, "Close these windows! Do you want the patient to freeze to death?"

As a result, when Sylvain got into practice, he didn't know which way to go. But he discovered an interesting home remedy after getting a call to see one particular Tonopah patient with pneumonia.

"I went in the patient's room and he's in bed, so I pulled back the covers from his chest. He had dead pigeons that had been split in half and placed on his chest as a poultice!" says Sylvain with a laugh. "I never saw that before or since. When I checked the patient the pigeons weren't warm, so they had been there for some time. Anyway, that patient didn't make it."

There wasn't much to do in the tiny town. Because Sylvain's office was located on the same floor as the Elks Club, he joined the organization and eventually became the exalted ruler of the Elks; he considers that achievement to be one of the high points of his life. Sometimes Sylvain and his friends would head out to the Silver Peak hot springs and swim. Once a year was the eagerly anticipated Goldfield Elks' Ball, an all-night party with an orchestra, and there was the Tonopah Elks' Ball as well.

Gambling had been legalized in Nevada in 1931, three years before Sylvain's arrival in Goldfield. He remembers that although he had no money, he did try his hand at a little gambling. But that ended quickly. "I found out I sure as hell couldn't afford to gamble, so I gave that up. I learned real early that you can't beat the game. As far as I'm concerned, gambling is strictly for the tourists—and I'm not a tourist."

During Sylvain's first year in town, a local young woman caught his eye. Ardis Laub had been born in Goldfield after her parents had emigrated from Germany, and her father ran the Goldfield butcher shop and grocery store, with Mrs. Laub helping him with the books and things of that sort, says Sylvain. Ardis' brother, Richard Laub, graduated from the University of Nevada, then went on to St. Louis University and became a doctor who later practiced in Las Vegas. Gerald and Ardis were married in 1935, and their first child, Marlene, was born in 1936.

Around 1935, Sylvain bought a General Electric X-ray machine for $1,000. Unwilling to go into debt, the decidedly unextravagant young doctor purchased it by cashing in an endowment policy his father had bought for him. Because the machine was small enough to carry around in his car, he was able to take X-rays in the patient's home, usually to diagnose fractures or to get a chest picture. He'd develop the film in his office and set the fractures. He would treat Colles' fractures, putting a plaster cast on the wrist and watching for complications, simple fractures like extremities and ribs, and occasionally a nasal fracture.

Because his practice was so slow, Sylvain decided to try to get a job as the county physician. The other doctor in town, Dr. George Francis Pierrot, was rather elderly. He was a county physician and health officer for Esmeralda County. Sylvain remembers thinking, "Gee, I would like to have that job too." He says the pay would have been a big help to his financial situation. So he approached the commissioner and asked him about his chances.

"The commissioner said, 'Well, if you register as a Democrat, I think I can help you get it.' That's how I've happened to register as a Democrat—and I have been one ever since, although I vote Republican," explains Sylvain with a laugh. The ambitious young physician's income rose to $225 a month, in addition to what he could make in private practice.

By that time, mining in Goldfield had dwindled, except for a fair amount of gold and silver mining activity developing nearby at Silver Peak, which stimulated the town just a little bit. Most of the local prospecting was done by ex-miners looking to find gold, who worked the claims themselves. They all paid a few dollars a month into a fund for Sylvain to treat them, usually for lacerations, an occasional foreign body in the eye, or minor problems.

A good number of Sylvain's male patients had silicosis along with pneumonia. Although Sylvain remembers silicosis as being a very serious thing in Nevada, it was non-compensatory while he was there (the occupational hazard law wasn't passed until after he left Goldfield). With no compensation, says Sylvain, "These guys who worked in the mines would get silicosis—and it was just too bad."

Many of the miners would contract silicosis after inhaling quartz dust, when dry drilling was used in the mines. After such exposure to silica, it frequently took years for lung changes to develop, Sylvain says. He remembers that some of the young miners used to tell him, "Well, we're going to beat that rap. We'll work a year or two and then we'll get out."

However, says Sylvain, a year or two was enough to get them loaded with silica. "Even though they didn't seem to be sick when they left, they'd eventually come down with silicosis," he says.

Fortunately, there wasn't much silicosis in Goldfield when Sylvain was practicing, because miners did wet drilling there instead of dry drilling, which reduced the amount of dust. The miners called silicosis "miner's con," meaning miner's consumption, whether they had TB (tuberculosis) or not. It didn't make much difference which disease they had, says Sylvain, since there was no treatment for either condition.

Sylvain says he didn't see many epidemic diseases, but did see some scarlet fever, usually in the spring and summer. Polio was a concern, and he saw some gonorrhea and syphilis. One thing that was different about southern Nevada was that prostitution was legal in many counties. In 1937, an aggressive venereal disease program was adopted by the state; the same year, the state Board of Health stipulated that prostitutes be examined weekly for gonorrhea, and have monthly blood tests for syphilis. (These venereal disease regulations continue today.)

In Goldfield, there was a house of prostitution, says Sylvain, and in Tonopah, just a half a block off the main street, was a house with a big line. In Goldfield, the prostitutes—referred to as "soiled doves" in those days—would come in to be checked by a doctor as required by law. The purpose of the exam was to rule out venereal disease and eliminate its transmission by the "soiled doves." Sylvain remembers the prostitutes as being nice patients to have, because he always got paid.

"They were very nice people. When we had our first child, they were very nice and they brought gifts," he remembers.

In those pre-sulfa days, men with syphilis were treated with salvarsen, and those with gonorrhea were treated with potassium permanganate (a colored antiseptic chemical) to irrigate the urethra of the penis. Sylvain says the attending physician who advised the use of weak solutions, rather than the very strong medications which caused strictures, taught him well.

"I think he was absolutely right. Why should a doctor irrigate and cause strictures with real strong medications? I feel it was correct, but I was never sure whether I had a cure or not. The sulfa drugs came out in '35, and then we finally had a way to specifically treat gonorrhea."

Those who were diagnosed with syphilis, an often fatal disease in those days, got a frank talk from Sylvain, who would tell them, "You have syphilis. It requires long-term therapy to get rid of it. You will have to have a shot once a week for eighteen months. If you decide to go on with this treatment we will keep a record, and if you ever leave town I'll give you a copy of the record. No matter where you go, the treatment will be the same. They will carry on with your treatment. If you aren't going to follow through with the whole treatment, you are better off not to have any treatment at all, because it interferes with your natural immunological process. Now that I've given you the story, do you want to be treated?"

The treatment consisted of intravenous neoarsphenamine and bismarsen or bismuth subsalicylate by intramuscular injection in the hip for eighteen months, once a week. Arsphenamine was also called 606;

Sylvain remembers that Dr. Cherry's car license plate bore the number 606 for years, until his death.

Sore throats were another common complaint. The sad part about it, notes Sylvain, was that when people came in with a sore throat, he didn't know if it was a strep throat or not. With no specific medication to kill the bacteria, it was always a very serious thing, he says, since strep bacteria could cause valvular heart disease and kidney disease.

Even though he was seeing patients with infectious diseases for which there was no treatment, the young doctor never worried about contracting a disease such as tuberculosis. But today, with the media informing the public of every virus, contagious disease, epidemic, or pandemic, Sylvain says that when he thinks about those diseases, he feels differently.

"In those days we should have been worried about TB, but we didn't seem to be worried—at least I never worried about it. I think starting now I'd be worried about everything."

After putting in five years in private practice in Goldfield, young Dr. Sylvain took a look at his situation—and a look at a future of more of the same—and was not entirely comfortable with what he saw. Dr. Pierrot, who practiced from a home office, was the other local sole practitioner; he did not have much business either, and didn't do obstetrics, recalls Sylvain. For five years Sylvain had tried his hardest to make a go of it, but his intuition told him it was best to make a break.

"There wasn't enough to do so I decided I'd better move," Sylvain explains. "I wasn't making any money either. I thought I might like public health work, because I thought the state needed a TB sanitarium. We had nothing—all our TB patients had to be shipped out of state."

Sylvain had heard there was going to be a scholarship available for someone interested in public health, so he wrote to Dr. Ed Hamer, the state health officer. As a result, the state paid for Sylvain's schooling. He chose the Rackham Graduate School at the University of Michigan, which was known to have a good school of public health.

"Dr. Hamer was a lot older than me, so I figured I would inherit his job. And it was such good pay—$300 a month! Back in those days you could live quite nicely on $300 a month, and save a little bit too," says Sylvain.

In the fall of 1939, Sylvain drove to Rackham at Ann Arbor. When he got there, he developed Bell's Palsy on the left side of his face. "It was a hell of a thing to enroll in school, to try and find a place to live, to have to eat in a restaurant and dribble all over the place," as he describes it.

"I got a little scared because it seemed to me the paralysis was lasting too long. So, I went to a couple of specialists and they said, 'You will probably make a full recovery,' which I did."

Finding a place to live in Ann Arbor was not easy for the young doctor, his wife, and their little girl. They finally found a place in an old building near the school with quarters on the first floor. On the floor above roomed Dr. Perkins, who was also there for a year to get public health training to become the Arizona state health officer.

Sylvain remembers an amusing anecdote from his venereal disease studies at Rackham, where gonorrhea was still treated through irrigation of the penis. "In Detroit I'd go to the clinic. It was kind of funny. Here's a whole trough, with four or five guys all lined up," he recalls, laughing at the image.

In Detroit, Sylvain was able to call on Dr. Gregory Grimaldi, with whom he had roomed during medical school and internship; Dr. Grimaldi had returned to his home town of Detroit to go into practice. Sylvain also recalls getting to see some good football at the University of Michigan with the headline-making All-American player, Tom Harmon. Dr. and Mrs. Sylvain would pack up and go to the football game and take their little girl along.

"It was quite an experience," recalls Sylvain. The man who blocked for Harmon was Forest Evashevski, who later coached football at the University of Iowa. "You never heard much about him but he was very important to Tom Harmon in those days."

In 1940, upon earning his master's degree in public health, Sylvain and his family left Ann Arbor and moved to Carson City. He went to work for the state health department as the state epidemiologist and director of local health.

An Office in the Capitol

1940–1942

As the Nevada state epidemiologist, Sylvain immediately began traveling all over Nevada doing tuberculin skin testing to see how many schoolchildren had been exposed to tuberculosis. He remembers that he was helped by a number of health professionals, including Dr. William Morris Little, director of the state health department's division of maternal and child health from 1940 to 1942. Another physician recalled by Sylvain was Dr. Burchard A. Winne; Dr. Winne's son, the late Dr. Burchard E. Winne, was a colon and rectal specialist before he died. Sylvain also recalls being helped by the division's nurse in charge of public health nurses, Christie Thompson.

"I bet I visited every school in the state," recalls Sylvain. Even in outlying areas, the students would be tested; in places like Tonopah, where they had mining, he recalls that they got a lot of positive skin reactions.

"This was an attempt to get enough data to convince the people that they needed a state TB sanitarium," notes Sylvain. His surveys confirmed that Nevada had a high tuberculosis rate, attributable to a diverse range of factors: it had few people, there was a high rate among the Native American population, and there was the mining problem, as Sylvain puts it. At that time, the United States Public Health Service was also interested in starting a public health department in Nevada, he says.

The Nevada Tuberculosis Association put in an application for a federal grant to aid in financing the construction of a fifty-bed tuberculosis hospital. The application was approved, Sylvain remembers, subject to the legislature's approval of the state's participation. Although a bill was prepared and introduced in the Legislature, Sylvain recalls, the hospital was never built.

Sylvain says when he came down to Las Vegas, the most important thing he had to do was to attempt to get a full-time city health department started. "I'd meet with the commissioners and so on. Nobody seemed to be interested, but my ace in the hole was George Franklin, since he was the most interested county commissioner. I was instrumental in developing the one down here," Sylvain recalls of the role he played in starting the full-time health department for Las Vegas.

When Sylvain had his office in the state capitol, Drs. James Thom and Fred Anderson were in Carson City as well. Dr. Thom had come to Las Vegas while working for the Industrial Commission. Sylvain says that John Sullivan, the director of vital statistics for the Nevada State Health Department for many years, was there for about a year before Sylvain arrived. Sylvain's secretary was Zelda Brown. Sylvain also recalls that Dr. Quannah McCall was doing dental work for the state and traveled with a dental trailer to see patients. Sylvain had met him while practicing in Goldfield, when McCall came through town and did some dental work. McCall practiced in Caliente, Sylvain believes, and eventually wound up with an office in Las Vegas; McCall has a daughter who is also practicing dentistry in Las Vegas, notes Sylvain.

The county health officer was Dr. Daniel J. Hurley, in Eureka, Nevada, who became state health officer and held that position for many years, Sylvain recalls. Hurley had gone to Harvard for his year of public health training after leaving Eureka, and later worked for the Atomic Energy Commission at Yucca Flats.

In Carson City, Sylvain was being groomed to succeed state health officer Dr. Hamer, who was getting up in years. Sylvain recalls that the understanding when they sent him to school was that he'd come back to go to work for the state health department for $300 a month. But on the day Sylvain moved into his office in the capitol, he got into a big fight with the governor. Sylvain can recall exactly how the governor stated his position.

"Governor Carville said, 'Doctor, we are not going to pay you $300 a month because that is the top salary here.' I said, 'You're not going to pay me $300 a month? You'll have my resignation in ten minutes. I'll go to the office and dictate it!' which I did. The day I show up, I resign the same day. I wonder what the governor was paid? The state health officer got $300, and the state engineer, I think, got $300," Sylvain asserts.

In the meanwhile, Sylvain got a phone call from Reno from the state sanitary engineer, William Wallace White. White told him, "Jerry, I was just told that you were going to quit. Jeez, don't fly off the handle like that! I'll see that you get your $300 a month. Come on over and see me."

Sylvain went over to see White and told him he would go back to work. The upshot: Sylvain got his $300 a month after all.

At about that time the Nevada Tuberculosis Association wanted him to do some liaison work for them, for which he recalls being paid $100 a month. State health officer Dr. Hamer, who was being paid $300 a month, broached the subject with Sylvain, saying, "You know, doctor, loyalty is an awful nice thing to have from people who work for you."

Sylvain answered, "Yes, doctor, I agree with you."

"I don't think you've been too loyal. You're getting more pay than I am," Hamer continued.

"Well," countered Sylvain, "It has nothing to do with loyalty. I'm getting the same as you, but I'm doing this extra work for the TB association." Sylvain says that kind of calmed things down.

For a short spell, Sylvain filled in as acting health officer, until one could be recruited from Las Vegas. He also had the venereal disease clinic, and his many duties required him to be on the road a great deal. One of his jobs was to call on all the doctors in Nevada; he estimates that at one time he knew every doctor in the state. While the job had its rewards, it required that he travel a good part of the time, which meant leaving his wife and their little girl in Carson City. After the birth of their second child, Gerald, in 1941, the constant separations became even more difficult.

"I kind of got sick of living that way, traveling all the time," he remembers. But, as members of the Sylvain clan had always done during times of hardship, Sylvain turned the scenario around to his advantage. He found something positive in a negative situation with the realization that the constant travel would give him a chance to look the state over. There were a few places that interested him.

He recalls that there was a good medical group in Elko that was quite well-recognized. The Elko clinic had been founded by Drs. George Collett, Dale Hadfield, Leslie A. Moren, and Robert P. Roantree; Drs. Charles Secor and Arthur J. Hood Sr. had been appointed associate members because of their ages and their desire to slow down in their practices. The town of Ely, also, had a good medical practice group, with head surgeon Dr. Ralph Bowdle, along with Drs. Noah Smernoff and William B. Ririe. Then there was the Las Vegas physicians' group, who had founded the Las Vegas Hospital and Clinic in 1933.

Sylvain decided Las Vegas would be more to his liking; having been born and raised in the northern part of the country, he was not anxious to return to cold weather and endure the harsh winters of Elko and Ely, and in his mind, Elko was kind of isolated. During a business trip, he stopped in at the Las Vegas Hospital and decided he liked the arrangement. Las Vegas Hospital was set up as a partnership with four doctors: Drs. Ray Balcom, Claire Woodbury, Stanley Hardy, and John Riley McDaniel.

Sylvain told Dr. Balcom, "Doctor, you know Dr. Mac (Dr. McDaniel) will be going into the service, and you're going to need some help here. I'd like very much to come down here and go to work."

"Oh," Dr. Balcom replied, "We don't need any help."

Sylvain said, "Well, if you ever decide you need help, would you remember that I'd like to come down here?"

Sylvain headed back to Carson City. By the time he got back, he had a phone call from Dr. Balcom, who asked just one question of Sylvain: "When can you come down?"

Practicing Family Medicine at Las Vegas Hospital and Clinic

1942–1944

LAS VEGAS, NEVADA

In March of 1942, just after turning thirty-three years old, Sylvain turned in his resignation and gave up his job as state epidemiologist. Leaving his wife, their daughter, and their baby son in Carson City, he headed south to go to work at Las Vegas Hospital and Clinic and to find housing for his family. Coincidentally, just one month later, in April of 1942, Dr. Cherry was appointed the only staff member of Las Vegas' Clark County General Hospital. Dr. Cherry had come down to Las Vegas from Tonopah to work as house physician and hospital administrator, for which he was being paid $150 a month. "You'll see Dr. Cherry's name on the building with the commissioners' names," notes Sylvain.

When Sylvain learned Dr. Cherry was living in a local hotel, he looked him up and they decided they'd room together. Neither one had their families there at the time. They'd get night calls, and if it was a paid patient, Sylvain would take it; if it was a county patient, Cherry would take it. The hotel was located within walking distances of Las Vegas Hospital, but Sylvain always drove because he needed the car for house calls.

In those days, the area known as the Strip gave no inkling of the glittering metropolis it would one day become. The El Rancho Vegas (located across the street from the current site of the Sahara Hotel) and the Last Frontier Hotel were the only hotels on a gravel road in a town populated by a colorful cast of characters. Tourists bound for Boulder Dam (now Hoover Dam) encountered grizzled prospectors, frontier businesspeople, prostitutes, transients, and Mormon farmers.

Then there were the casino workers, most of whom had learned their skills on the Monte Carlo and other offshore gambling ships anchored off Long Beach, California. Nevada had been given an edge just before the outbreak of World War II, when the state of California and the federal government banned gambling on the ships anchored off Santa Monica Pier and other California coastal areas. As a result, the ships' workers—and patrons—flocked to Nevada and to Las Vegas. (The legendary Sam Boyd, entrepreneur behind the Stardust, the Fremont and other gambling palaces, worked aboard the liners just before arriving in Las Vegas in 1941 with $80 to his name.)

Although the city was beginning its boom, its hospital facilities left much to be desired. Sylvain remembers that when he had visited Las Vegas several years earlier while with the health department, he had found very meager hospital facilities except for those at the Las Vegas Hospital and Clinic. The handful of hospitals serving Las Vegas included Boulder City Hospital, built in 1931 for $20,000 under the direction of Dr. John Riley McDaniel, who would become one of Sylvain's partners. The monthly cost of medical care for employees and their dependents of the six major companies building Boulder Dam (later renamed Hoover Dam) was a wallet-busting $1.50, paid through a payroll deduction. One of the construction companies was Kaiser Corporation, which later used the medical insurance payroll deduction in their Kaiser Permanente Plan. From 1943 to 1948 Boulder City Hospital re-opened, but only to treat wounded servicemen; a new hospital was not built until 1974.

Down the hill from Boulder City Hospital, surrounded by an eight-foot-high chain link fence, a "pest house" had been built to isolate infectious diseases. In one large room, cots were filled with patients suffering from smallpox, diphtheria, scarlet fever, and other contagious diseases. The entire complex was closed after completion of the dam.

Located on the grounds of what used to be the county poor farm, Clark County Indigent Hospital had been built by Clark County around 1931 to accommodate indigent patients from Las Vegas Hospital and the overflow from the crowded Boulder City Hospital. For the first few years, the county hospital was staffed by a single physician and one nurse on duty twenty-four hours a day, seven days a week. Renamed Clark County General Hospital, it struggled as a small, makeshift institution with forty beds, even though it began accepting private as well as county patients. Patients even overflowed into the halls of the crowded facility with the leaky roof. In 1956 the hospital's name was changed to Southern Nevada Memorial Hospital, and today it is called University Medical Center of Southern Nevada because of its affiliation with the University of Nevada School of Medicine.

Another hospital would be built soon after Sylvain's arrival. Basic Magnesium Incorporated, established in 1942 to mine a nearby titanium ore deposit, built its hospital during World War II for its employees in Henderson, as required by the federal government, and also served employees at the plants in Henderson producing war materials. But by 1949, defense contracts had dwindled, so that there was no longer support for the hospital. The facility was then purchased from the government for $1 by Mother Gerald Barry, who assumed all debts and agreed to provide twenty-five years of health care in the name of the Adrian Dominican Sisters. The Sisters, a religious order from Adrian, Michigan known for their successful experiences managing hospitals, then took charge. From 1972 to 1981, the hospital served as the Veterans Administration Outpatient Center. Later renamed Saint Rose Dominican Hospital, it is still referred to by longtime Las Vegans as Rose de Lima.

Fueled by the economic activity of World War II, the construction of Boulder Dam, and other factors, Las Vegas began an unprecedented period of accelerated growth. But despite the city's exploding population, housing was still affordable, as Sylvain soon discovered. He set about finding a place for his family. After seeing a nice house on Seventh Street with hardwood floors, a garage, a room in the basement, and a fenced yard, Sylvain decided he wanted to buy it.

"I think they wanted $12,000 and I said, 'Well, that's too much.' I offered them $10,000 and they took the $10,000. You can't buy a tent for that now!" says Sylvain, laughing. "In a short time, I was able to move my family down."

Sylvain remembers that very little surgery was actually done in town, with most of the work being done at Las Vegas Hospital and Clinic. The 25,000 square-foot building on the northeast corner of Eighth and Ogden was once Las Vegas' only hospital, and for years was the city's main hospital. The bustling facility had its humble origins in turn-of-the-century Las Vegas, which had neither a doctor nor a hospital until 1904, when a four-bed tent was set up in a railroad yard to treat Union Pacific employees. Dr. Royce Wood ("Roy") Martin, who had come to the frontier town just three months after its founding, moved the facility to an upstairs suite of offices in the Thomas Building at First and Fremont Streets in 1906; the expanded facility included a dozen beds and a pharmacy. In 1911, Martin and his colleague Dr. H.H. Clark made further improvements, including electric fans and appliances, an X-ray machine, and a kitchen. Martin subsequently converted the Palace Hotel on North Second Street to the Las Vegas Hospital in 1920, with eight rooms on the second floor plus an operating room.

But it was not until 1931, when Drs. Martin, Balcom, and F.M. Ferguson formed the Las Vegas Hospital Association, that the new two-story facility originally envisioned by Martin was constructed at 200 North Eighth Street for a cost of $100,000. The largest adobe building ever constructed in Las Vegas, the white building with the red tiled roof was designed in the popular style of the day, Mission Revival. It opened in December of 1931. In 1932, Dr. Claire Woodbury arrived and took over leadership with several other doctors, and the Association dissolved; Dr. Martin sold his interest in the hospital in 1937.

In the early 1940s, things in Las Vegas began to pick up, says Sylvain, with World War II and its associated activity. As a dramatic contrast to the slow pace and light patient load he had become accustomed to during his five years in sleepy Goldfield, Sylvain suddenly got very busy.

"When I came to Las Vegas in '42, I certainly didn't have to look for patients. We were busy all of the time. It wasn't like Goldfield. However, it was kind of rough after not being busy. I'd spend all day seeing patients. I'd go there in the morning and have breakfast about 9:00, then I'd have lunch there and I'd go home in the evening about 6:00; however, in those days, we made house calls, and also, I took turns being on call for the hospital at night. I'd get called for cut hands, injuries, automobile accidents—ordinary things, sickness and accidents. If an OB (obstetrics) patient came in, I'd go back to the hospital. We rotated emergency call, but we made our own house calls. I'd have a week on call for the emergency room and then I'd be off a week," remembers Sylvain. "It was quite a change."

Their emergency room was very busy, says Sylvain, because it was the only hospital in town that did everything. By that time there was no hospital in the nearby area of Boulder Dam, so all the related accidents and injuries were brought to the Las Vegas Hospital, Sylvain explains.

For a number of years Sylvain was also an examiner for the Selective Service Board; he still has his certificate, signed by Franklin D. Roosevelt, and another signed by Harry Truman. As one of the examining physicians for Clark County Local Board Number I in Nevada, he did examinations from 1942 to 1944.

During his first year in Las Vegas, Sylvain started doing electrocardiograms, tracings used in the diagnosis of heart disease. He remembers their first machine as being a Cambridge electrocardiograph, which actually photographed the oscillations on photosensitive paper. They'd develop the record like an X-ray by soaking it in development solution and hanging it up to dry before reading it. Sylvain praises the later addition of the direct writer as a tremendous boon and timesaver, because the Cambridge machine was very complicated to use.

With the war going on, all the Las Vegas Hospital doctors had signed up with the military procurement service, remembers Sylvain; they were never certain just when they might get tapped to go. That went on for two years. When they finally called Sylvain he said, "My God, I've been expecting this for two years. Why wasn't I called earlier?"

A Welcome Respite in the Navy

1944–1946

There was a good reason Sylvain had not been contacted earlier by the Navy. As the officer told him, "Well, you are the only one doing electrocardiograms and you are on the draft board as a review officer. That's why you didn't get called before."

Sylvain was in the U.S. Navy from 1944 until 1946. Because of his masters degree in public health from the University of Michigan, he was sent to Camp Lejeune, North Carolina, to be the officer in charge of the Navy Epidemiology Unit Number 21. The experience turned out to be a beautiful, much-needed two-year vacation for Sylvain.

"I had a lady marine chauffeur. I'd go to the office in the morning and I'd go to the golf course in the afternoon. That is what the degree from Michigan did for me. I feel I wouldn't be alive today if I hadn't had my two-year vacation," Sylvain admits frankly. "We were absolutely overworked in Las Vegas. We were short of doctors and we did everything, including house calls."

Home Again: Las Vegas Hospital and Clinic
1946–1976

After his discharge in 1946, Sylvain returned to a Las Vegas that was busting at the seams as a result of the massive postwar influx of ex-GIs pouring in to the city. Clark County Hospital hadn't been very busy before that, he says, but really got busy about the time he got out of the service. Sylvain returned to the fast pace of work at the Las Vegas Hospital and Clinic, and also continued doing Selective Service Board examinations when he was returned to inactive duty in the Reserve.

He remembers a number of doctors who were practicing at the time: one was railroad doctor Hale Slavin, who had come to town in 1934 and had a very busy practice. Dr. David Decatur Carr had become the second Clark County Health Officer, Sylvain recalls, succeeded by Dr. Otto Ravenholt.

"I remember when he came to Las Vegas to become the Clark County Health Officer. Frequently, he came over to visit and have lunch at the Las Vegas Hospital with Dr. Woodbury, who was on the State Board of Health. One of my other partners, Dr. Hardy, was on the Nevada State Board of Medical Examiners," Sylvain notes. He also remembers that Dr. Balcom, the doctor who originally hired Sylvain, had two stepsons who went on to practice in Reno, Dr. Morris and Dr. Dana Little.

By 1946, Drs. Wilmer Allen and Grant Lund had joined the Las Vegas Hospital partnership. Later, says Sylvain, they bought Dr. Balcom out and he moved to California, leaving six partners. They became known by the acronym "McWALSH" (Drs. McDaniel, Woodbury, Allen, Lund, Sylvain, and Hardy).

They bought some shares from the other doctors, so that eventually all were equal partners, with each drawing the same salary, says Sylvain. The general surgeon, Dr. Woodbury, also did urology. Dr. Hardy did general practice, but he also did a lot of fracture work, and McDaniel and Sylvain did general practice. Dr. Lund did only pediatrics, and Dr. Allen specialized in eye, ear, nose, and throat diseases. Drs. McDaniel, Hardy and Sylvain took emergency calls after office hours, unless it was an eye case, in which case they'd get Dr. Allen; children were seen by Dr. Lund. Drs. McDaniel, Hardy and Sylvain delivered most of the babies, with Dr. Woodbury doing an occasional delivery on the rare occasion when he was not busy with surgery. Sylvain assisted in surgery, did some minor surgery, and treated simple fractures with plaster casts.

During those postwar years, Sylvain was seeing about thirty patients a day—double the amount he saw in Goldfield—and most of them paid cash. There was very little insurance and no such thing as Medicare, which would not become law until the 1960s. Charges were only $3, $4, or $5 for office procedures. There were the usual general practice cases, patients with pneumonia, heart cases, some TB patients, diabetics, and patients with hypertension, for which there weren't too many drugs, Sylvain says. There were also the ulcer patients, Sylvain says. "The ulcer treatment was so miserable. We used milk and cream every half hour or so with antacids."

Before going into the Navy, Dr. Sylvain had delivered babies and cared for them as they grew into adulthood. When he returned in 1946, pediatrician Dr. Lund had joined the partnership, so he would take the kids after Sylvain delivered them. "When they turned twelve, I'd get them back. So, I didn't know how to handle pediatrics after awhile because he took care of them—and he did a good job, too," emphasizes Sylvain.

The Las Vegas Hospital and Clinic of the mid-1940s had three wards with about fifty beds, as Sylvain remembers. There was a big ward in the back that had quite a few beds in it, a smaller ward with four beds in the middle, the OB ward, and a few private rooms. The hospital was usually not full, he says. Most of the emergency room cases came to the hospital, with a lot of trauma cases, fractures, and lacerations. There weren't very many infectious disease cases in the hospital, because most of the contagious cases were treated at home, says Sylvain.

"As far as contagious diseases, well, we didn't actually quarantine them. We just said, 'Keep this child or adult at home, because this is a contagious disease.' And, it seems to me that if they had scarlet fever, we used to put a kind of sign on the door. But, even in Goldfield, of course, we didn't have a hospital, so those cases (measles, mumps and chicken pox) were treated in the home," recalls Sylvain.

Every spring Sylvain saw some polio cases in Las Vegas. The County Hospital eventually got an iron lung, but because the Las Vegas Hospital didn't have one, severe polio cases were sent down to California, recalls Sylvain.

"One of my patients had to be in an iron lung and since they were going to send him home from L.A., I went down to learn a little bit about how to take care of him. He was able to get out of the lung a little bit, but at night he'd always have to get back in the lung. His wife had a baby, so he was able to impregnate her. He lived quite a while, I don't remember how many years."

Sylvain says there were really good X-ray and laboratory facilities at the hospital. They had an X-ray technician and they could do fluoroscopes such as upper gastrointestinal studies, barium enemas, intravenous pyelograms to study the kidney, and gallbladder studies. They had trained laboratory personnel who could do blood counts and some other blood tests.

There was also a drug room. Hospital staff handled their own drugs, locking up the narcotics, Sylvain remembers. Every so often, though, they'd have a problem with missing narcotics. Even though a doctor would order a shot for a patient, it didn't seem to produce the desired effect, says Sylvain, adding, "It didn't work because the person giving the shot would take it themselves! So, after awhile, we'd catch up to the culprit."

Sylvain spent four weeks at Saranac Lake, New York at the Trudeau Research Laboratory for Tuberculosis and two weeks at Bellevue Hospital in New York City learning what was considered a revolutionary technique for that time. Artificial pneumothorax, or collapsing the lung, produced a pneumothorax by putting air in the chest to get a partial collapse of the lung. Sylvain estimates that he treated about twelve tuberculosis patients with a pneumothorax. The procedure consisted of placing a needle in the pleural space, taking a pressure reading, and pumping in room air. He says he knew how much air to put in because he kept a record, and never had complications because he was very careful. After putting the air in, they'd do fluoroscopy (X-raying a part of the body and recording the rays on a fluorescent screen in order to view the organ in motion). Eventually he'd get an X-ray so he'd have a record. He'd try to keep the pressure about the same, to keep the collapsed lung about where he wanted it.

At the beginning some patients would come in every week, but after awhile they'd come in every two or three weeks, as Sylvain remembers.

After the procedure, he explains, patients were no longer contagious: they weren't spitting out tubercular bacilli because the diseased part was collapsed. Dr. McDaniel also did the procedure, and to the best of Sylvain's knowledge, they were the only two doing them locally. Describing the method as good therapy, he says, "antibiotics were eventually developed for tuberculosis, and pneumothoraces were no longer necessary."

Years earlier, in Goldfield, some of the miners and the railroad employees Sylvain had taken care of had been covered by the Nevada Industrial Commission. Every once in a blue moon, says Sylvain, the industrial commissioner and his doctor would stop in Goldfield to interview him about patients. Later, at the Las Vegas Hospital, Sylvain again did Nevada Industrial Commission work. When a commission representative asked if Sylvain would be interested in becoming the local industrial commission doctor, he told him no but referred him to Dr. Richard Laub. Laub, Sylvain's brother-in-law, took the job and served as the industrial insurance doctor there for at least twenty years, Sylvain recalls.

Many industrial patients were unhappy and felt that services were not adequate, notes Sylvain. They complained, and the industrial commission asked the Nevada State Medical Association to review the cases. Three Las Vegas doctors were appointed by the Association to the Nevada Industrial Commission referee board: Drs. Kenneth F. Smith, Zigmunt Melvin Starzynski, and Sylvain.

"We called ourselves 'the three S's,' Sylvain remembers. "If a patient was unhappy, not getting along okay, he was referred to us. If we felt he needed further care, even if we had to refer the patient out of state, we'd make a recommendation and it was done. We were only supposed to serve one year, but we served many years, because nobody read the law to notice that we should be appointed every year."

What Sylvain finds interesting—and a sharp contrast to today's lawsuit-burdened judicial system—is that not one case went to court during the time the three doctors served. They would start by examining and questioning the patients; Sylvain emphasizes that the process was always very open.

"If they wanted to bring their lawyers in, they were allowed to. If they wanted to bring the union boss with them, we permitted it. They could bring anybody they wanted and nothing was secretive. It was all open," declares Sylvain. "All of the years that we were there we never once went to court; right after they changed the system, they began to go to court."

Sylvain also became involved in organized medicine, but he wanted to be more than simply a member: he always wanted to be involved as an officer. When he first came to Las Vegas in 1942, he joined the Clark County Medical Society, becoming president in 1947. He remembers that as president, he gave a speech when the Basic Magnesium Hospital was being turned over to the Dominican Sisters. He also belonged to the Nevada State Medical Association, and served as president in 1954. He was president of the Nevada Academy of Family Practice from 1954 to 1955, and has been a member of the AMA (American Medical Association) since becoming a licensed physician in 1934.

The years passed and Sylvain's children now numbered three: daughter Marlene and sons Gerald R. and Robert. But in 1960, just short of their twenty-fifth wedding anniversary, Ardis Sylvain died suddenly at the age of forty-seven. Sylvain was left a widower with three children.

"She wasn't sick," remembers Sylvain. "I mean, she never complained of being sick. The only complaint she had was every once in awhile she complained of a severe headache. That is the only complaint I can ever remember. And, we didn't do anything about it because it would quickly pass. I don't know whether she had a stroke or what. To this day, I just don't know. We would have been married twenty-five years. We missed our twenty-fifth anniversary by about two months."

When Ardis died, the Sylvains were living in a home on Sixth Street. Her mother moved in to take care of the Sylvains' youngest son, Robert, who was in grammar school. Their oldest son, Jerry, was a freshman attending his father's alma mater, Marquette University, and daughter Marlene had just graduated from the University of Arizona and was living in San Francisco.

After his wife died, Sylvain got acquainted over bridge with Zetta Starzynski, who had been divorced from Dr. Starzynski. Sylvain started taking her out and they later married; their marriage would last for thirty-seven years, until her death in 1997. Zetta had had two daughters from her previous marriage, Jill and Debbie, and she and Sylvain had a daughter, D'Anne.

As the city's population swelled—in just ten years, from 1960 to 1970, the 64,405 residents of Las Vegas doubled to reach a total of 125,787—there were many highlights in Sylvain's life. One was being named Nevada Physician of the Year in 1963 by pharmaceutical giant A.H. Robins, and another was his delivery of the only set of triplets ever born in the Las Vegas Hospital.

Sylvain remembers being very worried about the mother. He thought she was having hydramnios (a condition in which excess fluid surrounds the unborn child) because her abdomen was getting so big, and didn't realize she was carrying triplets until he X-rayed her, he recalls. "I knew I was going to have a problem with little tiny babies when she went into labor prematurely. I went to the pediatrician and I said, 'Look, Grant, I've got a patient that's going to have triplets. I want you there at the time of the delivery to take over the care of these triplets.'"

When Dr. Lund told Sylvain he'd better send the patient somewhere else, Sylvain told him that if he didn't want to be the pediatrician, he'd get somebody else. Dr. Lund showed up, as Sylvain puts it, then things really flew into fast gear. First, they had to alert the engineer so he could go to the county and get two incubators, because they only had one. Then the hospital also had a rule that a nurse had to be in attendance at all times, so they had to make sure they had enough nurses so none of the three babies would be alone at any time. But the babies were born and got along beautifully with no problems, even though they were very, very small, less than five pounds each. Sylvain remembers proudly that he had it all set up so things would go smoothly, and they did.

"The triplets graduated from high school in 1988. So, they're about twenty-one," he says, very much like a proud father.

Sylvain also remembers the time the mail brought a surprise from a woman he had delivered years before in Goldfield: she had sent him a money order for $50. Sylvain says the woman must have found out from her mother that her delivery had not been paid for—so she paid for it many years later—at the 1930s rate.

"When I left Goldfield, I had no records. If anybody owed me money, it was just forgotten. I remembered the mother when I got the money order; I forgot she hadn't paid, and therefore it wasn't a debt, because I didn't even know about it," Sylvain explains. He wondered if he should mail it back to her. Then he got to thinking that maybe he shouldn't send it back, because she wanted to feel like she'd been paid for, so he discussed this with a few people; taking their advice, he cashed the money order.

Over the decades, the hospital that had been Las Vegas' newest, most well-equipped facility underwent many changes. The partners bought out Dr. McDaniel, who went to work for the University of Wyoming. Sylvain says McDaniel didn't stay long, though; he returned to Nevada and opened an office in Fallon for awhile, then came back to Las Vegas to open an office. Finally, says Sylvain, McDaniel closed that office and came back to the Las Vegas Hospital.

In 1972, Dr. Gawinn Gardner and Dr. Kenneth Smith, whom Sylvain remembers as being chief surgeon at Rose de Lima Hospital, became interested in buying the hospital and building an addition. But the partners never gave it too much thought, says Sylvain, because they weren't too interested in making the institution any larger.

Sylvain continued working at the Las Vegas Hospital and Clinic throughout the early 1970s. But by 1974, the hospital was more than forty years old; it was in need of remodeling and new equipment, chief surgeon Dr. Woodbury became ill, and several of the partners were getting too old, Sylvain says. He remembers that Les Edwards, the administrator who had started at exactly the same time as Sylvain, was still working in 1974 when they decided to close the hospital. Sylvain continued practicing with Dr. Lund and Dr. Allen, and all three kept offices there until 1976. When Allen and Lund retired that year, the partners closed the building for good.

Full Circle: Returning to Practice as a Sole Practitioner

1976–1994

LAS VEGAS, NEVADA

Sylvain moved his practice in 1976 to an office on Sahara Rancho, where he continued to practice for another fourteen years. In 1990, he relocated to an office on West Charleston owned by his son, Gerald, who was practicing ophthalmology. Sylvain was a sole practitioner again, just as he had been in Goldfield.

He employed a secretary and a registered nurse. He was on the medical staffs of Sunrise Hospital and Valley Hospital so that he could hospitalize patients when necessary; if he had a surgical case, he'd refer his patient to a surgeon and then go in as an assistant surgeon to help with the surgery. Sylvain stopped doing pediatrics and obstetrics, having lost his familiarity with pediatrics because Dr. Lund had covered that for many years at Las Vegas Hospital and Clinic.

In the early years, the partners had taken turns being on call, but after returning to private practice Sylvain took only his calls. If his patients got sick and he wasn't available, he says, they were instructed to go to emergency. Sylvain says he was not interested in being very busy, and just wanted an adequate practice to make expenses to be happy; if he had to subsidize the office, he would quit. He did not want to retire because he still liked to practice a little bit, but he didn't want to work hard. Because he no longer went to the hospital, when he left the office he would go home.

He saw people with hypertension and some with cardiac problems. He liked doing physical examinations and also Federal Aviation Examinations, which he had been doing since 1942, because most of those people were well. Once in a while he would find something, but most of them were in pretty good shape, he says.

No longer a bustling health care facility, the once-respected Las Vegas Hospital and Clinic slipped into decline in its final years, first as the $45-a-week Oslo House motel, then as an abandoned, boarded-up eyesore. The building was declared a state historical monument in 1988—but just two months later, the forty-five-year-old landmark burned down. The neighborhood, just blocks from the downtown casino district, had gone down so badly that firefighters were routinely dousing blazes caused by vagrants who set fires to cook or keep warm. After the fire that consumed the abandoned hospital was extinguished, the body of a transient was found in the rubble.

Just after the fire, *Las Vegas Review-Journal* reporter Diane Russell spoke with the son of Dr. Stanley Hardy, one of Sylvain's partners. William Hardy said, "A piece of Las Vegas history just went down today. I was born here. My son was born here, as were some of the firefighters who fought this fire."

Sylvain commented at the time, "It was sad to close the hospital and sad to learn it had burned."

Dottie Pitzer, a registered nurse who worked with Sylvain for twenty-five years, has fond memories of both Las Vegas Hospital and in the office. She says Sylvain was the kindest man and the best doctor she has ever worked for or with, adding, "He took time with his patients—listened to them—and used to say you could help a patient more by just listening to them. The days of the general doctor who treats everything and everyone, from newborn to geriatrics, are gone. He did not overcharge, many times doing much for no charge. He was tops in my book, and you don't find them like him anymore. He was always willing to help if you had a problem."

"Oh, yes," Pitzer adds. "He loved parties. He was the perfect host—and usually the life of the party!"

Sylvain loved playing the comedian. Pitzer remembers that sometimes he would sneak up behind the nurses and yell in a moaning voice, "'Nurse!' Everyone would come from everywhere," she recalls.

Over the years, Sylvain watched his six children grow up; some chose medical careers like their father, and several chose to stay in Las Vegas. His oldest son, Gerald R. Sylvain, is an ophthalmologist and his grandson, Gerald Mark Sylvain, is an orthopedic surgeon, both in Las Vegas. His youngest son, Robert, a lawyer, also lives in Las Vegas. Marlene Varone, his daughter, makes her home in Santa Rosa, California. His daughter by his second marriage, D'Anne Walley, lives in Naples, Italy, where her husband is in the service, with their two children. Debbie Starzynski, one of Sylvain's stepdaughters, resides in northern California; his other stepdaughter, Jill Starzynski Robbins, lives in Virginia. Sylvain describes his family as being a real close-knit family, very much like the one in which he was raised.

"It's this kind of a combined family, because my first wife died when she was relatively young. My second wife, Zetta, had two daughters. But our combined family is close," says Sylvain. He says that his late wife Zetta did a real good job, and that it was one of their important goals in life to raise the family in such a way that they had no problems, like alcohol and narcotics and all that sort of thing—and they succeeded.

"I think I've been very, very fortunate. In this day and age, they tell me that by the time kids get to high school, they've already been into marijuana. I didn't have any problems—drugs or otherwise—with my children."

Other concerns Sylvain had while in practice also centered on his children: to have an adequate income to be able to send them to college, and not to become dependent on any of them when he retired. He wanted to have enough income so that he could enjoy a little travel, golf, and some of the other things he wanted to pursue after retirement. At one time, he says, he thought he'd like to learn to fly, but he didn't have enough money; by the time he had enough, he didn't have the time, and later, he wasn't interested.

Sometimes, on rare occasions, Sylvain would get away from the office to fit in a game of golf at the Muni, trying to play two or three times a week on his off days. When he first arrived, the Muni was the only golf course in the city. There were no golf carts in those days, Sylvain remembers, so the golfers would walk and push their little carts with their stick handles. A golf course was being developed there when Sylvain was still in Goldfield, he says, by Dr. Woodbury and other people interested in golf. They would be assigned to develop a green and take care of it, then another group of people developed another green.

By 1994, the year Sylvain celebrated his sixtieth year practicing medicine in Nevada, the population of southern Nevada had continued its breakneck pace of growth. The city of Las Vegas alone numbered more than 346,000, and the Las Vegas southern metropolitan area had 1,076,267 people. Sylvain, who turned eighty-five that year, was the only one of the McWALSH six from the Las Vegas Hospital and Clinic who was still alive, and he was still putting in four days a week in his office as a sole practitioner. But he found himself becoming more and more concerned about his patients. Because he would often find himself worrying about them after he left the office, he decided to retire in mid-

1994, and sold his practice to Dr. Ted Thorpe, a family practitioner. Sylvain says he was interested in selling the practice because he wanted to get rid of the records; as he explains, "You have to keep the records for at least five or six years if you close an office."

As for the Las Vegas Hospital and Clinic, the vacant land on which it had been situated was sold in late 1998, and affordable housing apartments will be built on the site. Five family members of the original doctors' partnership, including Dr. Sylvain, still owned the property when it was sold.

"It's going to be nice for the downtown area," said Dr. Stanley Hardy's son, William Hardy, the realtor who brokered the sale. At a recent get-together at Sylvain's home, Hardy reflected on the transaction. "We could've sold it a couple of times to somebody who was going to use it as a flophouse or something we wouldn't have been proud of. I felt it was a good thing for our property to be used for, and good for the community. We can leave a legacy."

Looking Back on Sixty Years as a Nevada Physician

1994–1999

Sylvain has been retired since mid-1994. Asked to assess his health today, he says, "My health? Well, I'm ninety years old. My health is fairly good. I wear hearing aids. I take medicine for hypertension and I have Type II diabetes; I take pills, but I don't watch my diet. I just figure, 'Oh, the hell with it, at my age,'" he says with a chuckle. "I do my blood sugars once in awhile and they're reasonable, as far as I'm concerned. I don't think my doctor's real happy, but I'm pretty happy with it."

He finally kicked his longtime smoking habit before undergoing carotid artery surgery, around fifteen years ago. As Sylvain says with pride, "I lit my last cigarette in the hospital and I said, 'I'm gonna quit when I leave here,' and I did—no trouble." Although he remains very active, some physical limitations have lingered on as a result of two strokes he suffered several years after retiring. One stroke caused him to lose feeling in the left side of his body, but true to character, he does not go on about his own personal health problems. While he hasn't been able to get back to golfing—yet—he declares that he's going to try it again. For the most part, Sylvain's memory and mental faculties are still amazingly sharp: He keeps up with the latest technological advances and engages in lively debates with other doctors about the controversial managed care phenomenon and other developments on the medical front.

Sylvain lives alone now, but with the companionship of his children and longtime close friends who live nearby, he still enjoys life and relishes that enjoyment. He is nostalgic for the Las Vegas that was, saying, "I think I liked the old days better because of the traffic, particularly. I hate the traffic." He still misses his late wife, Zetta, since her passing two years ago, but he remains warm, gracious, and fun-loving overall. He is in his element when entertaining, sipping a cocktail perched on a barstool at the well-stocked bar in his comfortable Las Vegas home. He loves a good party—and lots of belly laughs—as at his ninetieth birthday luncheon in January, 1999, when twenty-five nurses who worked with him at Las Vegas Hospital and Clinic gathered to celebrate and reminisce about old times.

Sylvain's daughter, Marlene Sylvain, remembers that when she used to go to his office to have lunch, he would run from his office to the kitchen as if he was competing in the 100-yard dash.

"When we go to lunch now, he still competes," notes Marlene, adding, "I wish I had his energy!"

Reflecting on his sixty years as a Nevada physician, Sylvain says simply, "I enjoyed what I was doing. I guess that's all I can tell you."

Since he enjoyed it so much, did it feel like work? Sylvain says it did—sometimes. "You know, you get called at night, you'd get tired and you'd get called—but you've got to do it. But I enjoyed the practice immensely—in those days. I don't think I'd enjoy it now."

For sixty years, Gerald Joseph Sylvain, M.D. served the community as a beloved Nevada family doctor. Perhaps the type of physician Sylvain was known and loved as was best described by his late wife, Zetta, before she died. She used to say Sylvain would go to any length to care for his patients. She liked to tell the story about the time one of his patients needed to go to the City of Hope in Los Angeles, but had no way of getting there. But for Dr. Sylvain, the solution was simple, according to Zetta.

"He said, 'Take my car,' and handed them the keys."

The visionary who built Las Vegas Hospital and Clinic, Dr. Royce W. "Roy" Martin, poses with Las Vegas socialite Alta Ham in 1929. Alta Ham's prominent early Las Vegas family members were major contributors to higher education in Las Vegas (University of Nevada, Las Vegas Special Collections photo).

Las Vegas Hospital and Clinic shortly after its 1931 opening. The structure was once the city's only hospital, and was, for years, the city's main hospital (University of Nevada, Las Vegas Special Collections photo).

Jack C. Cherry, M.D., 1978, house physician and hospital administrator of Clark County General Hospital, later renamed University Medical Center of Southern Nevada (Jack C. Cherry [son] photo).

Young Gerald Joseph Sylvain in Butte, Montana (Gerald J. Sylvain, M.D. photo).

Marquette University
freshman Gerald Sylvain
in 1926 (Gerald J. Sylvain,
M.D. photo).

Young Dr. Sylvain during his early years of general practice in sleepy Goldfield,
Nevada, in 1937 (Gerald J. Sylvain, M.D. photo).

Gerald Joseph Sylvain, M.D., Nevada State Epidemiologist and Director of Local Health from 1940 to 1942, at work in his Carson City, Nevada office (Gerald J. Sylvain, M.D. photo).

The dashing Dr. Sylvain in the late 1930s (Gerald J. Sylvain, M.D. photo).

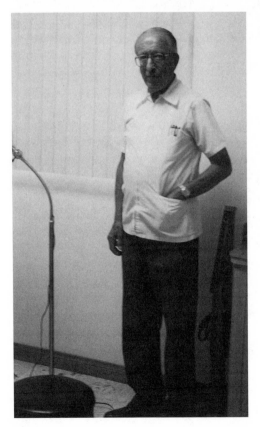

(top left) Gerald Joseph Sylvain, M.D., Nevada State Medical Association President, 1954-1955 (Nevada State Medical Association photo).

(top right) Gerald Joseph Sylvain, M.D., socializing at his Las Vegas home in 1998 (Photo by Annie Blachley).

(left) The doctor is in: Gerald Joseph Sylvain, M.D., in his West Charleston office in Las Vegas in 1991 (Gerald J. Sylvain, M.D. photo).

The family home in Sudlersville, Maryland where Joseph Matthias George, Jr. was born on May 20, 1913 (Joseph M. George, Jr., M.D. photo).

Toddler Joseph Matthias George, Jr. at age 18 months in 1915 (Joseph M. George, Jr., M.D. photo).

Joseph M. George, Jr., M.D., President, Nevada State Medical Association, in 1966 (Nevada State Medical Association photo).

Joseph M. George, Jr., M.D. and Dorothy M. O'Donnell at their wedding on October 22, 1950 (Dorothy M. George, R.N. photo).

(top) Captain Joseph M. George, Jr., M.D., U.S. Army Air Corps Flight Surgeon, in 1942 (Joseph M. George, Jr., M.D. photo) *(bottom)* Lieutenant Dorothy Marie O'Donnell, R.N., U.S. Army Nurse Corps, in 1945, before she met and married Joseph M. George, Jr., M.D (Dorothy M. George, R.N. photo).

Joseph M. George, Jr., M.D., President, Nevada State Medical Association, with Drs. Theodore Jacobs, Kirk Cammack, and Hugh Follmer in 1966 (University of Nevada School of Medicine Collection).

Dr. Joseph M. George, Jr.'s 80th birthday celebration, May, 1993. Front row, l-r: Joseph M. George, Jr. M.D.; Patricia George Meyers, daughter; Lyn Meyers Jefferson, daughter. Middle row, l-r: Dr. June George Bullion, daughter; Dorothy O'Donnell George, R.N., wife; Margaret George Quimby, daughter. Back row: Clyde Bullion, son-in-law; Janelle George DeCorte, daughter; Joseph M. George, Jr., son (Joseph M. George, M.D. photo).

2

Joseph Matthias George, Jr., M.D.

General Practitioner; Years Practiced: 1940–1988

"I've been delighted ever since I

matriculated into medical school,

and I've been delighted ever since."

—*Joseph M. George, Jr., M.D.*

A Town of 250 People Provides
a Strong Foundation

1913–1930

SUDLERSVILLE, MARYLAND

You can usually tell a lot about a person from the tone of the person's voice. It is no different with Dr. Joseph M. George, Jr. He speaks calmly, in a tone that sounds as if he's just pulled up an easy chair by the fire and is ready to settle down to a friendly chat. The art of conversation, which he obviously enjoys, comes easily to him.

His words roll out comfortably in a warm, slightly folksy style, with strong traces of his distinctive Baltimore area accent still popping up frequently. He is a longtime Nevada resident—has been for nearly sixty years now—but the early influences from back East remain strongly ingrained, even though they date back to a place and time when his life was vastly different. The close, loving environment that formed who George is was a very small town, with just 250 people.

It's called Sudlersville, that tiny village on the eastern shore of Maryland. Just a few miles to the east, beyond the Delaware border, lies Delaware Bay, with its fishing and oystering people; a mile to the west is Chesapeake Bay. For generations, most of the townsfolk of Sudlersville have been farmers, tending the fertile land between the two bays, growing and harvesting their crops of corn, wheat and oats.

Sudlersville, like so many other small communities, has its own cemetery. The headstones mark the final resting places of its farmers and schoolteachers and shopkeepers and just about all the other people in town, including the ancestors of the George family. Starting with Joe George's great great grandfather, born in 1801, every one of the George family ancestors has been buried at the Sudlersville cemetery.

In the 1800s, the people of Sudlersville tended not to stray very far from home; before automobile and airplane travel became common, the family connections were rather extensive locally. People living there would usually marry people close by, geographically, and it was a pretty homogeneous type of a family arrangement. The family Joe George, Jr. was born into was no exception: all the people in the George family had come from that same area for at least two centuries. His father, Joseph George, Sr., had been born in Sudlersville in 1888. Joe's uncle by marriage, Dr. Foster Sudler, had also been born there in the 1800s, and had married Joe's father's oldest sister, Elsie.

The fact that Joe's uncle was the only doctor in town would no doubt influence his young nephew's future: the young George boy would go on to a career in medicine also, and would remain in practice for fifty years as an old-fashioned family doctor who cared for his patients at all stages of their lives. Joe's uncle, educated at Jefferson Medical School in Philadelphia, practiced general medicine; in those early days of medicine before the dawn of specialization, pretty near everyone in the smaller areas had to practice general medicine or starve to death.

On May 20, 1913, Uncle Foster Sudler got the word that Lilian Nelson George, his brother-in-law's wife, was ready to give birth. Uncle Sudler safely delivered little Joseph George, Jr.; in keeping with the custom those days, Joe was born at his parents' home. With the addition of its newest resident, the population of the town of Sudlersville now numbered 250.

Joe was raised by parents who demonstrated a strong religious belief and work ethic. His mother, originally from Baltimore, had graduated from Western Maryland Methodist College to become a schoolteacher in Sudlersville before meeting his father; she later became a contented housewife, he says. His father owned a grain elevator that took in all the various crops for the farmers, in addition to an insurance business. The people in the community were ninety-nine percent Methodist, he recalls, and most were very strict Methodists, including his father.

"The people in the community were very staunch Methodists and very ethical people. That's the atmosphere I was raised in," George recalls.

Joe's childhood was uneventful except for the death of Uncle Sudler when Joe was six years old; his uncle died of tuberculosis, which was both common and fatal in those days. The rest of Joe's boyhood was spent growing up with his parents and all his other relatives and friends nearby in the safe, nurturing town. Unlike so many young people raised in our large, modern cities who frequently find themselves tormented by self-doubt, mired in angst, and agonizing about what their future may hold for them, Joe George always knew exactly what he wanted to be:

even very early in his schooling, by grammar school, he started thinking he wanted to be a doctor.

"I just was always interested in medicine, and I liked to do experiments in chemistry and Lord knows what on my own, and not in school. So I just gravitated towards it," recalls George.

He says there were chemistry kits you could buy that interested him, with their little packages of various types of chemicals and the directions of what you could mix to make whatever you wanted.

"I enjoyed doing those experiments. That was highly fascinating to me," George remembers. Because he liked chemistry so much, no one would have batted an eyelash had he chosen to become a research scientist or a chemist instead of a doctor. But he had one reason, a clear understanding of why he chose the profession he did, which has endured throughout his life —and it speaks volumes about just who he is.

"I'm a people-oriented person. I've always been a people-oriented person. I was raised in a town of 250 people in a farming community, and my whole orientation has been towards people," George explains. "I went into family practice because I did not want to go into a specialty where you saw a person once or twice and never saw them again, like you do with surgery, or what have you. So as a consequence, I went into family medicine—and I've loved it all of my life."

George went to high school at Sudlersville High with the kids he had known all his life. The tiny town grew slightly, during those years; by the time George turned fourteen years of age in 1927, there were 276 people living in Sudlersville. By that time, he had firmed up his decision to go into medicine. He recalls most of the kids in his high school as being farm kids who were not particularly interested in biology or the chemistry type of subjects; they were contented to stay on the farm, he recalls. But he was different. After graduating from Sudlersville High in 1930 in a class of fifteen, George enrolled in the University of Pennsylvania in nearby Philadelphia as a premedical student.

A String of Stool Samples, a Tuxedoed Mentor, and Solo Practice

1930—1943

PHILADELPHIA, PENNSYLVANIA
BALTIMORE, MARYLAND
SUDLERSVILLE, MARYLAND

At the University of Pennsylvania, George majored in biology and the biology courses in zoology; he says the courses in the various aspects of biology were always highly interesting to him. After graduating from the University in 1934, he applied to the University of Maryland medical school and was accepted. He didn't have to travel very far to attend, for the school was just a short hop across Chesapeake Bay, just west of Sudlersville. His education was now on the fast track, as was his personal life; by 1934, he was a husband and father. His first daughter, Margaret, was born in 1934.

George remembers that he was thrilled to be attending medical school. As he so aptly phrases it, "I've been delighted ever since I matriculated in medical school in 1934, and I've been delighted ever since."

The concept of medical ethics was drummed into the students constantly at medical school, recalls George. That emphasis, combined with the staunch Methodist influence of his upbringing, helped cement the foundation for his dedicated work ethic and sense of honesty. George explains it by stating simply, "From my standpoint, there was only one way to go."

The students were taught across the board in those days, he explains; there was no emphasis whatsoever on specialization. George explains that at the University of Maryland, they felt very strongly that whether you went into psychiatry, or surgery, or family practice, or whatever, you should have a very broad background in medicine.

"As a matter of fact, most doctors did a general internship afterwards, even if they were going into surgery or some other field, to give them a broader viewpoint as they went down their career. In my class —I don't know the precise percentage—but I would say that probably fifty percent

54

of them went into specialties, and a very large percent were general types of physicians," notes George.

George graduated from medical school in 1938 in a class of an even one hundred. He and his wife had a second daughter, Patricia, in 1937. Continuing his medical education with a two-year rotating internship/residency at the University of Maryland Hospital in Baltimore, George says that the rotating type of residency was really a godsend. Although going through all the various specialties was not required by law in those days, he felt it was quite proper to do, and says he has always been extremely happy that he did. Yet despite his thorough exposure to all the specialties, George was never tempted to specialize: unwavering, he held fast to his childhood dream of becoming a family doctor, so that he could live his dream and take care of his patients from cradle to grave.

George remembers that the teaching staff at the University of Maryland was mainly part-time, consisting of doctors who had their own practices, rather than full-time medical people who were at a medical school for the sole purpose of teaching. He says that many were very outstanding private practitioners in the area, in all sorts of fields.

"I've thoroughly revered most all of them down through the years because they really were superlative people, individually as well as professionally," George states.

While completing his residency, George would meet Dr. Maurice Pincoffs, the man he still considers to be one of his strongest mentors. To this day George still has strong memories of the fantastic wartime experiences told to him by Dr. Pincoffs, his professor of medicine. The professor would tell George about the World War I years, when he had been an ambulance driver in France and Belgium. But it was as an all-around role model that the professor made the most indelible impression on young Dr. George—through his actions, not his words.

"He was really inspiring to me. He pretty near worked me to death when I was on his service, but I had the highest respect for him and still do. He always inspired me," remarks George.

"Dr. Pincoffs had three full-time careers, all at the same time: he was a professor of medicine, he had a huge private practice at the University Hospital, and he was also head of the Maryland State Board of Health. All of these things were full-time careers actually, plus being the editor of *The Annals of Internal Medicine*, which is still one of the fine medical journals," says George, adding, "How he got everything accomplished I've never understood; he didn't get much sleep."

In those days, George explains, because the lab at the hospital was only open from eight in the morning to five o'clock at night, the residents working at night had to do all their own lab work.

"Anything after five, the house staff did: if it was somebody in a diabetic coma who came in, you did the blood sugar, you did everything. If they came in with a lobar pneumonia, in those days you had to identify the bacteria. You had to get the specimen, and you had to take it down to the lab and type the particular type of pneumococcus (the bacterium associated with pneumonia) that you were dealing with, because some types had a serum that you could use, and some didn't," George explains.

One particular night stands out in George's memory. It was nearly midnight, and he was working at the lab when Dr. Pincoffs stopped by the hospital. The professor had been working late at the state board of health and came in to the lab wearing a tuxedo, George recalls.

"In those days, you had a string of stool specimens and a string of urine specimens that you had to do before you went to bed. He took off his coat, and he helped me do every last one of them—and I never forgot it," remembers George. "People like that just inspire you tremendously."

After completing his residency, George went back home to Sudlersville and started general practice as a sole practitioner in 1940. In those simpler pre-World War II years, when credit cards had not yet become a staple and a crutch of the American economy, his patients paid for their office visits with cash, because practically no one had medical insurance at all. George remembers that when he first started practice in Sudlersville, he charged a dollar an office visit—and that included supplying patients with their medicine.

"We kept a pharmacy at our offices because drugstores were few and far between. But the medicine that they got, whatever it was, came out of that dollar office fee—so you didn't make much money back in those days, I can tell you. I grossed $6,000 a year, with my expenses taken out of that great sum," George recalls.

When he first started in practice, they didn't have penicillin or any of the antibiotics; all doctors had was the early stages of the sulfa drugs, George explains. "If you had a streptococcus (a type of bacteria that may cause severe infections in humans) blood poisoning, the death rate was virtually 100 percent. And now it's almost been wiped out."

George recalls that in 1939, just before sulfa was produced in the United States, one of his patients was treated at the University of Maryland Hospital with sulfa that had been brought in a suitcase from Germany by a professor at Johns Hopkins University.

"Thank the Lord there was no FDA (Food and Drug Administration) and clinical trials, or that patient of mine would never have survived," George says.

While the sulfa drugs were not antibiotics, explains George, they were antibacterial. He says the sulfa drugs were a great help in certain cases, but in a large percentage of cases, there were no drugs to take care of infections. Whether a patient had a pneumonia or some other ailment, they were treated with nothing other than aspirin or things of that sort, he says. He says that later, when the sulfa drugs came in, sulfa drugs would work on some pneumonias, but didn't help other pneumonias at all—and doctors had nothing else to offer beyond that.

"After World War II, the lobar pneunomias were treated with penicillin with an oxygen tent which, fortunately, we no longer have to use," George explains. "But the methods of treating then were much more crude than they are today. With a lot of pneumonias now, you don't even go into the hospital, even though they're fairly severe."

George remembers that in the early 1940s, very few patients went into the hospital, even if they were very sick. Doctors would hospitalize patients for an appendectomy or for similar procedures, but as far as the medically ill, very few went in unless they were awfully far gone, George remembers.

"We saw a fair number with tuberculosis, because it was pretty prevalent in most places," George recalls. "The programs to take care of people with tuberculosis had not been advanced very far. On the East Coast, if a person could afford it, they went up to Saranac, New York or down to Asheville, North Carolina, in the mountains. That was supposed to be the place to go for treatment of tuberculosis, but most people couldn't afford that type of thing."

In the West, there were tuberculosis hospitals or sanitariums in every large city, for those who could afford to stay there as inpatients. As George puts it, they had to do the best they could. "Unfortunately, a lot of family members caught the disease. If grandma had tuberculosis, she spread it to the kids and the grandkids, because for the most part, they stayed at home," he explains.

"We had no specific medications for tuberculosis. All you had was fresh air and encouragement and not much else to treat it by. Later, pneumothorax came in, which helped some but not totally, and then they did thorocoplasties. They collapsed the chest on the involved side, but treatment was very nonspecific, to say the least," George observes.

He recalls that doctors in those days saw a lot of the usual things that still continue to plague people today: colds, bronchitis, sore throats, and all those types of things. "There were a lot of lobar pneumonias," George adds.

In 1940, while in practice in Sudlersville, the Georges' third child, Joseph M. George, 3rd, came along; their next child, Lyn, was born in 1942. But although he could not suspect what the future held in store, George would soon be forced to bid farewell to his wife and their four children, to his practice, and to his beloved home town. An escalating situation halfway across the world would change George's life forever.

By the early 1940s, World War II was at its peak. So, with just two years of private practice behind him, George enlisted in the service and left Sudlersville. He went into the United States Army Air Corps in July of 1942 at West Palm Beach, Florida. In those days, recalls George, it was called the Army Air Corps; after the war, it became the U.S. Air Force, formed as a separate branch of the service. The Army Air Corps sent George through flight surgeon school at Randolph Field in San Antonio, Texas, in late 1942. After graduating in 1943 as a flight surgeon, he shipped out to London and North Africa, where he would spend the last years of the war.

A Fish out of Water: Behind the Lines During Wartime

1943–1945

ENGLAND

NORTH AFRICA

FLORIDA

As a flight surgeon, George's first overseas assignment was London, England. He recalls that the Army Air Corps was usually stationed considerably behind the lines, in London, in this case, so that its overseas flight surgeons could be with the heavy bombers (B-17s and B-24s). Because those were long-range bombers, the servicemen were kept in England and North Africa, he says. For flight surgeons, George remembers, the emphasis was on the flying crews and not on the ground crews, although they did take care of the ground crewmen who came in on sick call as well. But the doctors' main job was to take care of the various members of the flight crews, from the pilots to the gunners.

When Captain George arrived in London, it was March of 1943 and he had not yet turned thirty. His memories of that first wartime experience—a total blackout in a war-ravaged Great Britain that had been valiantly battling the Germans since 1939—are still vivid. He says, candidly, "You feel like a fish out of water, because you don't know anything."

They had arrived after dark and didn't even know where they were, or where the air raid shelter was at the billet (the military lodging in a private building). George says they couldn't even light a cigarette on the street or anything of that sort, because the flare of a light or a match was a tip-off to the German bombers that there were people there.

"We were put up at a billet in London and they had nothing to eat. So we had to go looking for a place to eat—but with no lights on, and no knowledge of the city, and no British money. It took us some while to find a place where we could eat," George remembers. He still recalls that the only items on the menu were pigeons and Welsh rarebit (a dish of melted cheese, often mixed with ale or beer, served on crackers or toast).

George remembers that the first night they were there, the air raid siren went off; fortunately, he says, there was a chap downstairs who worked there and he directed them to the air raid shelter.

"The British people who worked there never called you 'lieutenant;' they always called you '"leftenant,"'" George remembers.

The next day, when they emerged from the billet, they saw what had not been visible the night before: previous bombings had wiped out the two buildings on either side of the billet in which they had stayed. Both buildings were completely gone, destroyed by the heavy bombing rained down on London by the Germans during the early years of the conflict.

"That kind of gave you a little pause, too," admits George.

The Germans' primary target in England was London, says George, although they bombed targets in Liverpool and other places as well. The three-and-a-half years he spent on active duty during the horrific conflict would prove to be a crucial test of his mettle. Yet, as it was with his work ethic, there was really no question as to whether he would hold up through it all. As he says, matter-of-factly, "You took it as it came: you had no choice, actually."

As the war dragged on, the strain of war got to many in the military— but George was one of those lucky ones who came out of the conflict unscathed; he maintains that he enjoyed his work as a flight surgeon. During those years, the flight crews did a lot of bombing runs under severe conditions, George remembers.

"On some raids, you had huge numbers of planes that didn't come back—and some came back all shot up. But you did what you had to do in taking care of them."

After completing his tour of duty in London and North Africa, George's last duty station was at a psychiatric hospital in the Tampa-St. Petersburg area in Florida, where the people sent back as psychiatric casualties from the war zones were treated.

"Of the chaps who were subjected to this type of psychological abuse, actually a few of them cracked over there, but not too many. Once they came back to the States, they went all to pieces," George remembers.

Some of the patients brought down to the hospital were treated for three or four weeks, some for several months. But those soldiers requiring the most care were not the ones who came in as casualties of the bombing raids in Europe, but those who came back from very remote areas, George explains.

"Some of the worst ones I had had been in Greenland and the Aleutian Islands and what have you in those isolated areas, and that duty really got to them. They were the ones who had gone rather stir-crazy from their tremendous isolation in those areas."

The hospital to which George was assigned was quite full, with some three hundred patients there who all exhibited psychiatric problems of one sort or another, he remembers. His commanding officer was Colonel Roy Grinker, a very eminent psychiatrist and neurologist. As a civilian, Colonel Grinker had been the head of Michael Reese Psychiatric Hospital in Chicago, which was a big psychiatric hospital then and still is today, George points out.

"We had a superb commanding officer in Roy Grinker. In fact, he had written the textbook we used in medical school to study neurology," recalls George.

"There are psychiatrists and there are psychiatrists—but he had very good common sense. If you had a problem in treating a patient, you'd go up to visit him in his office, and he was more than happy to help you and tell you what was the best way to proceed."

In September of 1945, George was discharged from the service in St. Petersburg, Florida. He had three months of terminal leave due, during which he did sick call for Nellis Air Force Base. In December of 1945, he got out of the service for good.

A Sal Sagev Hotel Bellhop Seals
the Doctor's Destiny
1945–1946

LAS VEGAS, NEVADA

Many of the patients George treated while the war was going on in Europe and after the war back in the States were suffering from the psychological strains of battle or isolation. But in the aftermath, many who had served in the military found their lives torn apart in other ways. George was one of those. "During the war my practice was totally gone," he explains. Because there was no one to take over the practice when he enlisted in the service, he had been forced to close down his office—after only two years of practicing solo in Sudlersville.

When he had closed his practice and enlisted, he had no way of predicting that the prolonged time he would spend in the service would lead to the irreparable damage of yet another aspect of his life: his marriage. As he puts it, the long wartime separation caused the discontinuation of his marital relationship. By the time he was discharged from the service, he realized that his own family—his wife and their four children—had become what he calls casualties of the war. As a result, George and his wife divorced.

At that point, robbed of both his medical practice and his family, he found himself at a major turning point in his life. But he knew one thing for certain: he didn't want to go back into isolated country practice. He decided he wanted to set about rebuilding his life in a completely new environment.

"I was looking for a place to practice and wound up, just by good fortune, in Las Vegas. Actually, I didn't come to Las Vegas. I was heading to California."

While George was in the service, a lot of the fellows he knew in the medical field had told him they were going to California after the war, he says. He had never been there and knew nothing about it, but he figured that California would probably be as good a place as any to practice. So he headed to the train station and caught the Union Pacific to Los Angeles. On the way, people on the train started talking about Las Vegas. There was plenty to talk about in those post-World War II years, with the state of Nevada managing to overshadow neighboring California in many aspects. Unlike California, the silver state had divorce laws that were so scandalously liberal that there were contingents back East who wanted Nevada's statehood revoked. Adding to Nevada's reputation was prostitution, which was conducted legally in more than half the counties in the state. The topper, though, was the gambling, which was legal throughout the entire state; the taxes paid by the gambling industry lowered the tax burden of Nevadans, making it among the lowest in the country and providing a huge economic incentive.

The train George took west had to stop in Las Vegas. As George describes, the steam engines had to get filled up with water before they made the hump of the Sierra Nevada going west into California. He recalls that the Las Vegas train station was located where the Union Plaza Hotel now stands. He describes it as a rather pretty train station, with a big area in front of it with grass; a park-like facility, he recalls it as being quite attractive. During the forty-five minutes that the train was stopped in Las Vegas, everybody poured off the train to Fremont Street to play the slot machines

"There were plenty of them there, right on Fremont Street," George recalls with a laugh.

George stopped at the first place he came to, across from the station, at the corner of Main Street and Fremont. It was the Sal Sagev Hotel (Sal Sagev is Las Vegas spelled backwards, as old-time Las Vegans know). At the hotel, George chanced to bump into a bellhop. That brief encounter would change the course of his life forever.

"I was still in uniform, of course, so the bellhop there saw my caduceus on my blouse. He asked me where I was going to practice. Actually, I told him I was on the way to California. He said, 'We need doctors here,'" George recalls.

One thing led to another, and during that chance conversation, George was persuaded to go over to the desk to see if they had any rooms. The hotel was small, as were all the hotels in town in those days—before the proliferation of mega-resorts throughout Las Vegas— so rooms were very much in demand. Guests could only stay for three days because the hotels needed the turnover. Fortunately for George, there was a room available. So he went back to the station, grabbed his

B-4 bag off the train, brought it back, and stayed in the hotel to look the town over for a few days. He held on to his train ticket from Las Vegas to Los Angeles, his original destination.

When his reservation was up at the Sal Sagev Hotel, George recalls, he had to look for another place. He found a boarding house on Third Street that had an empty room. He started talking to various druggists and others around town, including Elliott King, a pharmacist at the City Drugstore on the corner of Third and Fremont Streets. King had just been discharged from the Army Air Corps Gunnery School, which later became Nellis Air Force Base, in the desert near Las Vegas, recalls George.

"King had spent most all the war stationed there, and they had taught machine gunnery to gunners and various members of the flight crews. Elliott persuaded me to stay and apply to the state board for my licensure. I applied and went up to Carson City by bus on February 4, 1946 and then I, fortunately, was given a license," George remembers. Several years later, that same pharmacist would again have a major influence on George's destiny.

That same day, George came back and opened up his office, which he had already arranged for. It was located downtown at 402 Carson, at Fourth and Carson Street (the present location of the Nevada State Bank). He was living on Third Street. He recalls that old Mr. Laraby had built a number of small apartment houses, separate houses a few feet apart, and George had one of those.

"It worked out very well," George remembers. He stayed in his office location for fourteen years—and never did use that train ticket from Las Vegas to Los Angeles.

Thirteen Doctors, Two Hospitals, and the Sixteen-Hour Work Day

1946–1965

LAS VEGAS, NEVADA

Fresh out of the service, George opened up his Las Vegas office in 1946. The city had some 15,000 people, including North Las Vegas, which would later became a separate city. There were only two main hospitals in Las Vegas proper then—Las Vegas Hospital and Clinic, and Clark County General Hospital, which had originated as Clark County Indigent Hospital. It would be later be renamed Southern Nevada Memorial Hospital and then University Medical Center of Southern Nevada, as it is currently known. Basic Magnesium Hospital, built during World War II in Henderson, Nevada, would close in 1949, to reopen later as Saint Rose de Lima; it would then be renamed Saint Rose Dominican Hospital, its current name.

When George opened his practice in Las Vegas, the city had just thirteen doctors. George recalls that Dr. Jack Cherry had moved down from Tonopah in 1942 to work as house physician and administrator of Clark County General Hospital. Because George did not know the territory or Nevada itself very well when he arrived, he was happy to have Dr. Cherry advise him on a number of things.

"I always appreciated his advice over the years. Dr. Cherry was somewhat of a controversial doctor because he graduated from Kansas City Medical College, an unaccredited school. I considered that he practiced a very good brand of medicine. Las Vegas Hospital was a private hospital right downtown at Eighth and Ogden, and the six doctors who owned it didn't get along very well with Dr. Cherry because they didn't want that kind of competition, which is understandable," George explains.

"All of them were good friends of mine, and I don't say that there was competition, but that was the basis of it," he adds.

During the earlier years in practice, George did not go to Las Vegas Hospital, he says, because the six doctors at the private hospital could handle everything themselves without any trouble.

"Later, they were happy to have somebody come in and deliver babies there and help them keep their beds filled and use other facilities of theirs. They were Dr. Gerald J. Sylvain, Dr. Stanley Hardy, Dr. Claire Woodbury, Dr. Wilmer Allen, Dr. Grant Lund, and Dr. John McDaniel," George says.

Two of the Las Vegas Hospital doctors were still in the service: Dr. Gerald J. Sylvain, who was still in the navy, and Dr. John McDaniel, who was still in the Army Air Corps; both would return to Las Vegas Hospital after being discharged from the service. As George recalls, both doctors subsequently became presidents of the Nevada State Medical Association. The rest of the doctors, such as Dr. Cherry, were in town because there were no doctors up in the more rural areas like Overton (about fifty miles northeast of Las Vegas) at that time, says George.

"I did office hours twice a week up to Overton at that time to cover, because there was no medical facility up there at all," notes George. He remembers that even just thirty years ago, in the late 1960s, there was virtually nothing out in Pahrump (some fifty miles west of Las Vegas), either; he says they were raising cotton in those days and they had a cotton gin to process the cotton.

George remembers taking care of a great many people from that area and delivering a lot of babies for women from both Mesquite and Overton, both northeast of Las Vegas. He says patients would come down either to Clark County General Hospital or Rose de Lima Hospital in Henderson.

"They ran a very fine facility out there and I delivered a lot of babies out there," George recalls. He says that in those days, he could make the run from his office at 402 Carson to Rose de Lima Hospital in twelve minutes. But as the years went by, it took much longer because of increased traffic and traffic lights. As George points out, "Now, with a red light and a siren, you couldn't make it in a half an hour!"

The young doctor did have one ace in the hole, though. "George Mayberry was the state highway patrolman for that route. I delivered four babies for him and his wife, Helen. He knew my car, so when he saw me driving fast towards Henderson, he would fall in ahead of me with sirens and flashing red lights and escort me to Rose de Lima Hospital there," George remembers. "It pays to have good friends."

George had night hours in Overton in 1946 and 1947, which made for a lot of driving. He can remember one night in particular in 1946, when he was treating a little girl who had severe stridor (loud, harsh breathing caused by failure of the larynx to be open sufficiently during respiration).

"I drove her and her mother to Clark County General Hospital. Her shortness of breath worsened and I had to do a tracheostomy (a surgical incision into the trachea, or windpipe, performed to relieve obstruction in breathing; a tube is inserted through the neck to keep the incision open) on arriving at the hospital. The tests revealed diphtheria," says George. (Diphtheria is an acute contagious disease characterized by weakness, high fever, and the formation in the air passages of a tough, membrane-like obstruction to breathing.)

"Fortunately, she survived. I haven't seen a case of diphtheria since."

At first, when George needed to get from his downtown office out to Clark County General, he would take the bus there and back—a rather inconvenient arrangement, to say the least. George explains that he couldn't get a car right after World War II in 1946, because cars weren't made during the war. He says it was six months before he could get himself a car.

"But I finally was able to get a Club Coupe Plymouth. It had 78,000 on the odometer. What the actual mileage was, I have no way of knowing. Fortunately, it ran well and took care of things very well for several years," he remembers.

As a new physician in town, George promptly joined the Clark County Medical Society, and became president in 1953. Because there weren't very many doctors in town at the time, the Society was not actually chartered by the Nevada State Medical Association until 1955. "In those days they didn't have so much incorporation and all the formalities, because there really wasn't any need for it until the mid-'50s," explains George.

He remembers that at most of the Medical Society meetings there were generally speakers on some medical topic of general interest. George says the discussions would include such things as drawing up an average fee scale. The doctors were not required to stay within it, but at least they would have a guideline, particularly as the new doctors came in, he explains. This would help in many ways to standardize the charges, says George.

"Later, they ran into problems of the federal government claiming price-fixing. You couldn't make out a scale of that sort anymore because of some lawsuits scattered around the country. They felt that it kept the doctors charging more, which I think is not true—but that was the argument."

Joseph Matthias George, Jr., M.D.   67

Meetings were quite small, as George remembers, because there weren't very many doctors in town. But all of the doctors were members of the Society, he says, including the doctors in town and in Boulder City, where Dr. Donald Maxwell MacCornack and Dr. Eugene Andrew MacCornack practiced. George recalls that Dr. Don had been out in Boulder City for many years. Dr. Don's brother, Dr. E.A. MacCornack, had been in South America and had come to the area to retire and to go into active practice with Dr. Don, says George.

The Society met for several years at the Nevada Biltmore Hotel, at Main Street and Bonanza, George recalls; the hotel had been built by entertainer Horace Hite, who had a band called Horace Hite and His Musical Knights, one of the big bands that was popular before World War II. George recalls that the Society then met for a number of years at the Las Vegas Municipal Golf Course.

"Dr. Claire Woodbury was one of the very active people who got the Las Vegas Municipal Golf Course going. It had a very nice clubhouse which was plenty big enough for those days. The Clark County Medical Society had a very active ladies auxiliary and they met at the Municipal Golf Course in a separate room from us; as a matter of fact, we moved out to the golf course club house, particularly to accommodate having the women meet at the same time, and it really worked out extremely well. The ladies' auxiliary old-timers here still are very good friends."

Regarding the golf course, George makes a statement that dispels a popular perception among the public that doctors spend most of their time playing golf rather than with their patients. As George explains, "I've never played golf, so I've really not been to courses, except mostly to clubhouses."

During those busy years when George was building his practice in Las Vegas, he didn't have a lot of time to spend on hobbies, or on much of anything else. His long, full work day would usually start at around 6:00 in the morning with hospital rounds; however, if he was assisting in surgery, he would have to be in the operating room an hour earlier, at 5:00 A.M. He would then head over to his office to see patients all day during office hours, catching up on correspondence, mail, and phone calls. Finishing up at the office around 6:15 at night, it would then be time to make evening hospital rounds. He would usually get home for supper around 7:00 or 8:00 P.M. Because he was on call, there were usually many babies to deliver at night. His average work day lasted anywhere from thirteen to sixteen hours.

With a schedule like that, there was little time for socializing other than at the hospital. In the late 1940s, though, George happened to strike up a conversation with registered nurse Dorothy O'Donnell. She was working as an obstetrical nurse at Clark County General, where he was delivering babies. The two would soon find out that they had a great deal in common.

Just as George had always wanted to be a doctor, Dorothy Marie O'Donnell had always wanted to be a nurse. As she says, "I wanted to take care of people and be a bedside nurse, and that's what I was."

Like George, who grew up in a small farming community, O'Donnell was raised on a farm in a little town in Wisconsin; she remembers taking countless pictures of the cows on the farm, as required by the dairy industry.

O'Donnell received her nurses' training at Saint Mary's Hospital in Rochester, Minnesota, graduating in 1943. During that pre-World War II era, nurses were taught to do everything, she remembers. In the morning, they bathed patients, gave them backrubs, and changed linens. Before the patients napped or were prepared for sleep at night, nurses again gave them backrubs, turned them, and made them comfortable. Nurses changed linens twice a day—more often if necessary—and were responsible for treatments and medications as well as bedside care. Because of the severe shortage of registered nurses (R.N.s) during the war, nurses worked twelve hours a day, six days a week, for which they earned $125 a month, recalls O'Donnell.

Just as George had been stationed overseas during World War II, O'Donnell served with the U.S. Army Nurse Corps in Okinawa. She was in charge of a makeshift orthopedic ward, a tent much like a M.A.S.H. unit. She remembers the time a typhoon hit the island, washing everything into the China Sea. The nurses moved all the patients on litters into caves in the side of the hill until the storm abated, when the patients could be evacuated to stateside hospitals.

"It was very hard work, but you couldn't leave them there in the beds, nor do any nursing care of the wounded, because the tents and everything washed out to sea," she recalls.

After peace was declared, she spent ten months as an army nurse in Japan with the Occupational Forces. Following her 1946 discharge, she went home to Wisconsin, then headed to California to work as a nurse. But as California was not in a hurry to clear outside nurses for duty, she stopped in Las Vegas. It was there she ended up getting sidetracked on her way to Los Angeles in much the same way as George had the year before. She had stopped in Las Vegas to see pharmacist Elliott King, whom she had known in high school back in her home town in Wisconsin. King was also the cousin of another R.N. with whom O'Donnell was traveling. By this time, King had become good friends with the new doctor in town, Joe George.

While she was waiting for the registration paperwork in California to go through, Nevada promptly cleared her for her license; because Nevada needed nurses desperately, she went to work at Rose de Lima Hospital for awhile. Then the chief of nurses at Clark County General, Mary Kennedy, heard about her being in town and asked if she'd like to come to work; the county hospital needed nurses badly at the time.

O'Donnell recalls that there were probably only twenty to thirty nurses for the whole of Clark County General when she started working there; when she was on night duty, there were only two nurses. They did labor rooms, delivery rooms, floor work and the nursery, and in the daytime they had about six or seven nurses on duty covering all of the above duties. The afternoon shift had three or four nurses. Nurses typically worked eight-hour shifts, six days a week, earning around $250 a month, she says.

"Nurses didn't complain a great deal in those days. They were very content to be helping people, because that was why they went into the nursing profession," she explains. "There were no such things as unions for nurses, strikes, etc., to interfere with nursing care."

During the several years she worked obstetrics at Clark County General from 11:00 P.M. to 7:00 A.M., Dorothy had more than one conversation with George, the doctor on call, while he was waiting for babies to deliver. By that time, Dorothy and the R.N. she had traveled to Las Vegas with were living in an apartment on North Sixteenth Street.

"It worked out extremely well, as far as I was concerned," George recalls with a smile. The conversations between Dorothy and George blossomed, and in 1950 they tied the knot and she became Dorothy O'Donnell George.

In those early years, when George was delivering babies, there was no specific person to give an anesthetic, he recalls. The nurse who was in the delivery room poured a little ether on a mask, and that was it, as George says.

"You didn't put them to sleep—you just eased their discomfort a bit while they were in the delivery process. The anesthesiologists disdained giving anesthetics for obstetrics I think, as much as anything, because it would mean they had to get up at night, et cetera, et cetera, and they figured that the operating room was enough."

George says he found obstetrics extremely satisfying. He estimates that he delivered more than 6,000 babies in town over a period of nearly thirty years, and many more before coming to Las Vegas.

"I delivered many patients multiple times and, of course, I would take care of the babies. I took care of the whole family down through the years, and I just don't see how you can do an enjoyable practice where you get a segment of a family, or a segment of the practice of medicine. I just enjoyed all the different types of medicine," says George.

"I took care of families over a prolonged period," he adds. "Because of that, you're happy to get up at 2:00 A.M. to go stitch up somebody or take care of a bellyache or heart involvement or whatever. So I never resented it; I was perfectly content to do so."

He can remember that in the 1940s, he charged anywhere from $50 to $100 for total obstetrical care; that included prenatal care, the delivery, and six weeks post-delivery. Now, as he notes, the cost is around $1,500. He recalls delivering quite a few at Rose de Lima Hospital for the Catholic Community Welfare for Monsignor Don Carmody, for $50 total; he says that Father Carmody was a close friend and he was glad to handle the deliveries for him.

"I delivered thousands of babies here, and in the early days there was no insurance to cover delivery at all. Of course, our prices weren't very great either," George points out. He recalls that by the 1950s, insurance had picked up considerably, in part because the unions came in and got stronger; insurance was carried through the unions for many workmen. The basic insurance ratio went up steadily from that time. He estimates that by 1955, probably a quarter of his patients were covered by insurance for deliveries, when the charge was $100. By the time he left practice, a great percentage of people had insurance, he says.

For an office visit in the 1940s, George had charged $3; in the early 1950s, that went up to five, he says, and six in the late '50s. "But I don't think until the mid-1970s I ever had a fee for an office call of more than ten dollars, which was standard in those days," George notes. When George retired from his Las Vegas practice in 1988, the charge was $12; that was still considered a real bargain when compared to what general practitioners had been charging a decade or so earlier, in 1976, in southern California: $18 for an office visit.

Because of the location of his office, George saw quite a few patients from the hotels downtown, and a few from the Strip, which was considered to be far out in those days.

"Now it is anything but far out," says George with a laugh. His patients came from downtown hotels such as the Golden Nugget and also the Apache, which later became the Horseshoe.

"Most of the people I took care of were anything from carpenters to all sorts of tradespeople," he explains. "My practice here was much like you'd have anywhere, with an extra sprinkling of the more exotic people from the casinos and what have you."

At first, George saw a lot of characters that typified the old Las Vegas, which in 1950 was still so small that motorists driving to the city would often go right past it. The Strip featured businesses such as realtor Helen Herr's real estate office with its sign proclaiming, "Las Vegas—Founded but Unbounded." A great force in Las Vegas real estate, Herr went on to become the first woman state senator in Nevada.

Many of George's patients during his early years in practice were quite different from the types of people he had known growing up and practicing in that small town back East. He recalls that many of his patients would barter for services, like the mechanic who would fix the doctor's car for a credit on his account. George notes that the Internal Revenue Service wasn't active in that sort of field in those days, and didn't make any to-do about it.

There was another patient he remembers, a chap who was an artist who would go out and paint desert scenes. Then the painter would come to town and get on a toot , as George tells it, and run out of money, so he would pay his doctor bill with those paintings. George says with a laugh, "They were nice paintings. I still have one out in my TV room."

He remembers other patients that embodied the mystique of the wild West and early Las Vegas, such as the prospectors. "There was an old Spanish war veteran who prospected all over heck and back, and every Christmas he would come in and bring us desert holly, a desert plant which is illegal to get anymore," George recalls. "It made lovely wreaths."

Another one of his more colorful patients owned a local casino and bar and used to come into the office with a bodyguard and a huge dog, George recalls. The casino owner would usually make a scene, he says. "He was a drunk, and with maybe five or six people in the waiting room, he'd shout at the top of his lungs, 'I need a shot of vitamin B!'"

"You didn't see that sort of thing in the later years. But there were a lot of characters here from the old Las Vegas," George recalls.

Some of the patients George took care of were married former prostitutes who became very stalwart citizens, he says, adding that quite a few of the prostitutes married Las Vegas old-timers. He remembers that on Las Vegas' North First Street, Block Sixteen had been a house of prostitution until Nellis Air Force Base, formerly the Army Air Corps Gunnery School, was built. Years before, during the construction of Hoover Dam in the early 1930s, brothel prostitution had operated openly in Block Sixteen and was well-patronized. But during World Wars I and II, although the federal government ordered Nevada and other states to suppress prostitution near military bases and installations, prostitution continued to flourish—in secret and without government regulation. Eventually, Block Sixteen was eliminated, and brothel prostitution became illegal in Las Vegas and Clark County.

"The army required that that be closed—but that didn't stop prostitution. That didn't shut down the Strip hotels, because they needed to supply various things to customers. They didn't necessarily have any official prostitutes that worked for the hotels, but the hotels kind of closed their eyes to the fact. I think it was the same in Reno and maybe Elko," says George.

"Not all the ladies of the night disappeared. A lot of them stayed in town. They were just not concentrated in one facility."

Fortunately, says George, treatment of infectious diseases, including venereal disease, was greatly improved with the development of penicillin during World War II. But before the longer-acting type of penicillin was developed, it had to be given by injection every three hours, George explains.

"If a person came in with an early case of syphilis, the health department didn't take care of them; they were taken care of by the individual doctors. You had to give a patient a shot every three hours, night and day, for two weeks, which got to be rather a considerable chore," he says.

He remembers that the health department was on the corner of Second and Stewart. The doctor who took care of it had been in the military, and it was several years before the department got a full-time doctor, George explains.

"Dr. Ravenholt has been here for the past thirty-five years or so, and has done a tremendous job. But the early facility was small and they didn't cover a great deal, except for shots for infants and things of that sort. There was a Dr. Anderson, and I forget who the doctor was who preceded Dr. Ravenholt at the health department, but Dr. Mark Herman was one of them."

Because of the hotels in town, George would see workmen's compensations cases; an example would be when a chef would cut his hand slicing meat and the hotel would refer him to George. His wife also remembers that there were a lot of dancers, too.

"We took care of their normal ailments and pregnancies. A lot of dancers on the Strip were regulars; they had been there for years. They had normal family lives and I took care of a great many of them and delivered quite a few of them," George remembers.

The number of doctors grew rapidly after the war, notes George: in 1946, Dr. Ken Smith and Dr. Harry E. Fightlin came to town, as did Dr. Chester Clinton Lockwood. George remembers that Dr. Lockwood was president of the Clark County Medical Society in 1954. Other doctors who moved to Las Vegas after World War II included Dr. Harold Boyer, who is still in practice in dermatology, and Dr. Emil Francis Cava. Dr. Cava came to town in 1953, as George remembers.

"He was our first OB-GYN (obstetrics and gynecology) specialist. The various ones that came in certainly were a tremendous asset to the community. Dr. Cava died of cancer a couple of years ago. He was a dear friend, as is Dr. Boyer," says George.

For many years, there were no emergency room physicians in town, so all the doctors would rotate through the alphabet on a twenty-four-hour basis, George recalls.

"Dr. Boyer, for instance, a dermatologist, would see the patients and if it was something that he felt was not something he should temporarily take care of overnight, he would call one of us and we would come in and see the patient for him. If there was a baby coming, I'll guarantee you he called in a hurry! We got a lot of unregistered pregnant mothers who came in who were in labor. No prenatal care, no regular doctor or anything—so you scrambled," George remembers.

"I can remember once the nurse called Dr. Lockwood (an ophthalmologist [eye specialist]) because this girl was about to deliver and had just come in. The nurse who called me was crying, and asked me if I could come over to deliver the baby because Dr. Lockwood had said he couldn't deliver a baby and had said, 'Why, I wouldn't know which end the baby comes out of'—which of course was stretching a bit. But what he was intending to say, of course, was that he didn't have much expertise in that field," explains George with a big laugh. "So I went over and took care of it."

As a young general practitioner, George branched out and became involved with many different organizations in the rapidly growing community he now called home. A member of the American Medical Association, he also belonged to the American Academy of Family Physicians, serving as president of the Nevada chapter in 1955. He demonstrated his concern for young people by working with several organizations focusing on youth. George was appointed one of the seven members of the City of Las Vegas Child Welfare Board; members regularly inspected child care homes of all sizes. From 1950 to 1976, he and other board members visited applicants and made recommendations for acceptance, rejection, or changes. During that period, from 1951 to 1954, he also worked with the Clark County Juvenile Probation Board, appointed by the Clark County Commission. The board heard the cases of juvenile offenders for minor offenses, says George, and advised the penalties and supervised probation.

From 1948 to 1986 he was a senior aviation medical examiner for the Federal Aviation Administration and from 1948 to 1951 was major and commander of the Las Vegas, Nevada National Guard Medical Detachment; a life member of the Veterans of Foreign Wars of the United States (V.F.W.), he served as state commander from 1951 to 1952 and national surgeon general from 1954 to 1955. In his capacity as V.F.W. state commander, George had to cover all over the state, he explains, and had to fly up and back for special occasions in Reno.

"The weather conditions, with high winds and so forth, were rougher in Bonanza Air Lines planes because of the difficulty with the old DC-3s. It was C-47s in the service and DC-3 in the civilian, but flying was usually around 15,000 feet between here and Reno—and because of that, when there was any considerable windy weather you got shaken up. Yet it was a real advantage, timewise," George says.

George was on the executive committee of the Nevada State Medical Association, he recalls, when Dr. Jerry Sylvain was state president, in the mid-1950s. They would fly up to Reno together on Bonanza.

"Dick Laub, who was raised in Goldfield, oftentimes was with us. He was a brother-in-law of Dr. Sylvain and Dr. Laub knew every back road in Nye County and Esmeralda County. Those planes flew so slow you could point out all sorts of things and have discussions about them on the way. But it was a disadvantage from the standpoint of the roughness of the flights and the time involved to get there, all of two-and-a-half hours each way. Later, when I was president of the Nevada State Medical Association in 1966, they flew the old DC-9s," George recalls.

By 1955, the year that Nevada's gaming board was created, Las Vegas had fifty-five doctors; George confirmed this recently by consulting a 1955 Las Vegas phone book. The dizzying rate of growth continued in the city, despite some setbacks, George remembers.

"I think it was 1957; three hotels ran into financial difficulties and closed. That put a crimp on the town temporarily, but it wasn't very long before they started rebuilding the present hotels and then adding more. So it's been really pretty much a boom ever since."

With the rapid rise in population, more hospitals were needed. Clark County General Hospital, known today as University Medical Center of Southern Nevada (UMC), did not have too many beds at first, George recalls.

"There were three wings: one was surgical, one was medical, and one was OB-GYN and pediatrics. There were probably thirty to thirty-five beds on each wing," as he remembers. George makes the observation that UMC has had to take a wider variety of doctors, but has an excellent staff. He says, "I've always been very happy with UMC, and if I had to go into a hospital now, I'd go into UMC."

George was chief of staff at UMC in 1953. He recalls that at that time the hospital staff had total autonomy.

"There was no outside interference that way. The seat of government, as far as the state was concerned, was Carson City, which was almost 450 miles north. As a consequence, except for the county and the city elections, you didn't get involved," explains George. "As for chief of staff, it wasn't interfered with except by local medical politics, but not by other outside politics."

In 1958, George and four other doctors served on the first credentials committee for a new Las Vegas hospital. The new facility, Sunrise Hospital, was a proprietary hospital (for-profit, owned by investors).

"We approved all the doctors that we considered qualified, and it has built up hugely since then," observes George. As the hospital got busier and the city's population kept rising dramatically, his practice continued to grow as well. But in just a few short years, proposed legislation would have a major impact on George's practice—and on the lives of virtually every health care provider and patient in the country.

Medicare, Medicaid, and Medical Practice in a Litigious Society

1965–1988

LAS VEGAS, NEVADA

Around the early 1960s, the medical political scene involved a new proposal in Congress: Medicare. Medicare, a national health program, would use federal, mostly social security funds, to cover certain medical and hospital expenses of the aged and the needy. It would forever change the face of medicine.

"Most of the doctors were extremely leery of Medicare and what it might bring, and our prediction was that it was going to be a real problem in the future—and the future has certainly borne that out," notes George.

"The real problem is—and this is partly encouragement from the Federal government and the way they handle it—the decisions are particularly made not by medical personnel per se, but oftentimes by clerks who are not very hip on diagnosis and that sort of thing," George asserts.

After George and Dorothy became partners in marriage, they also became partners in a line of work that is fast disappearing: solo general practice. Dorothy O'Donnell George assisted her husband throughout most of his forty-two years in practice in Las Vegas, as secretary, receptionist, nurse—and, she adds with a smile, "occasional janitor."

"I couldn't have done my practice well without my wife, Dorothy. She kept things coordinated," he says.

Being a sole practitioner had its advantages, like getting to know the patients well. He remembers that he and Dorothy had many favorite patients and that there were a lot of patients that they thoroughly enjoyed, he says.

But the fact that George was a sole practitioner made him particularly vulnerable to the paperwork nightmares encountered when submitting bills for his office charges to Medicare and Medicaid (Medicaid was the state of Nevada's public health program for those patients having no income or a low income). After Medicare and Medicaid became law on July 30, 1965, the Georges found they were running into all sorts of problems in the office with bills they had sent in being kicked back: the clerks at Medicare—who were usually neither doctors nor nurses—didn't understand what the coding meant.

"They would write back and say, 'What do you mean by coding this in this way?' Of course, that put a lot of extra work on Dorothy in the office, because she was forever having to explain to various personnel in Reno, or Phoenix, or wherever, what the procedure was—and why it was not something that they suggested that the coding should be."

Trying to collect fees on services he provided for patients with Medicaid insurance was also a chore. To justify a $12 charge, for instance, George remembers that the letters that he had to write would sometimes run six, eight, or even ten pages on a single office visit—and re-submissions of claims also required that copies of the chart notes from the office visit be attached. Once a month, Medicaid would send a check for around $3 on the $12 charge. As a result, in Las Vegas and throughout the country, many doctors had to increase the charges to their non-Medicaid patients to absorb the amounts written off because of nonpayment of Medicaid billings, just to stay in practice.

"It wasn't worth it," states George. "A lot of them, we didn't even bill for. You just felt like saying the heck with it, forget it. I don't know what the current formula is, but at that time, the state paid fifty-four cents on the dollar of whatever the authorized fee was. By the time you got your fee cut in half—and then even that was questioned—you got so that you weren't very enthusiastic about taking patients on," George explains.

"Doctors of my vintage have had many discussions about how medicine has changed during the time we practiced, and we universally felt that we'd practiced medicine in the golden era of medicine," George asserts.

"You didn't have all the regulations. Practically no one was covered by insurance, so you didn't have to fill out insurance papers. Nobody raised a fuss about 'you should have given this instead of that,' and all the rest of it. I think most of the doctors practiced a pretty good brand of medicine—but without all the regulation that is prevalent today," explains George.

In the days when George was practicing, he also made a lot of house calls; he says it would have been a disservice not to. But today, the house call scenario has changed. As George says, "If you have a person who's had a stroke and is mainly bedfast, to get medical care in somebody's office you've got to get a Medi-Car, all these other things. To me, it's ridiculous. It's a waste of human resources and money—but the Federal government doesn't seem to care."

He adds that when he would call on patients at the convalescent center, he would take his kit over and stitch them up if they fell out of bed and needed two or three stitches.

"I would sew them up right over there," George says. "Now, they call an ambulance, they take them to the hospital, they X-ray their head, they do all these other things. It's really, to me, a very expensive way to run medicine."

While many contemporary doctors practice this conservative type of medicine to cover all their bases in case they are sued, George is of the opinion that there is another reason. As he says, "They don't want to be bothered, either."

George states that the practice of medicine has also changed in the area of malpractice insurance (malpractice is defined as the injurious or unprofessional treatment—or culpable neglect—of a patient by a physician). He remembers that in the early days, malpractice suits were rare, and if someone sued it was for relatively small amounts. He carried no malpractice insurance for his first several years of practice because, he says, it really wasn't needed. He recalls getting his first malpractice insurance in the early 1950s through the American Academy of Family Physicians (AAFP).

"It cost me $39 a year, which by today's standards is virtually nothing. That was for $100,000/300,000 insurance. I carried my insurance through the AAFP clear until the late 1960s, when they discontinued carrying it because the costs had gotten very prohibitive," says George. "Then I went with St. Paul, which cost me roughly $175 a year as late as the late 1960s."

The rates skyrocketed as the years went by, says George; he adds that malpractice premiums today are almost prohibitive in some specialties. An illustration of this is the fact that many general practitioners in southern California, west of Las Vegas, were forced to stop assisting in surgery altogether by the mid-1970s. They could no longer afford to do so because the cost of premiums covering surgical assisting was so high.

But when George was practicing, he was able to continue assisting in surgery until he retired, most likely because Nevada malpractice insurance and litigation practices did not increase as drastically—and as rapidly—as in southern California. George says he almost always assisted

on his own patients and on a lot of others as well. However, George recalls that despite the fact that he had never had a claim during his forty-two years of practice in Las Vegas, his 1988 malpractice premium cost him $3,500 per year—for the lowest class of insurance.

At the root of the escalation in malpractice premiums was the increase in the number of people hiring attorneys to sue physicians or corporations or any entity perceived as having deep pockets (a hefty amount of insurance coverage). George sums up the present state of our litigious society by saying, "I don't think there's any question that the trial lawyers have opened the wedge, and now it's almost unlimited."

One reason trial lawyers began getting busier and busier was patient dissatisfaction, which often arises when families are not closely involved when a family member is ill. George maintains that it used to be that families were much more involved with patient care.

"Some families are extremely attentive to their families. Any time a family member is sick, whether they are old or young, they spend a huge amount of time and effort taking care of them. Others, unfortunately, feel the call of the Bingo tables or the slots. They neglect their families because of that—both physically and financially."

But in a city where gambling is all-pervasive, it is not only patients and their families who are affected. There have also been doctors who couldn't handle the games of chance, as George discovered when he was interviewing and monitoring doctors for many years for the Nevada State Board of Medical Examiners.

"We've had a few over the years that couldn't handle the gambling. In this town, if you can't handle gambling, you'd better get the heck out. Most people who live here on a permanent basis just don't gamble," he asserts. Saying that he never preferred to be on the Board, he thinks overall they've done a pretty good job.

"To a certain extent there is resentment from monitorees, although you try to be reasonable. Somebody's got to look over their shoulder to be able to report back to the State Board," he insists. "Sometimes it's individual doctors who have been appointed to keep an eye on them. Sometimes it's a committee of three, which I personally prefer because that way they can't point a finger at you that you're being biased, but for the most part I think that it's worked out pretty well."

In Las Vegas, as in any city, there were also those physicians who became alcohol-impaired. George says, however, that many of them have been rehabilitated, fortunately, and have done pretty well over the longer period of time.

"I don't think Las Vegas has a problem to any greater extent than else-where. We had problems with some while I was still in the service. I don't know that we had any greater percentage of difficulty here with doctors, as compared to most other areas."

As George and his wife watched the parameters of running their prac-tice change with the times, their own situation changed on the home front. They adopted two daughters: Janelle, in 1953, and June, in 1956. Janelle and June went to Gorman High School.

"They had parties at home," Dorothy says. "They didn't go out to the hotels much in those days; we didn't go, either. We took them to some of the good shows but they were 'good' shows. We didn't stay for the gambling, and they never participated in any, even after they were grown."

The Georges raised their children in a city that was undergoing a monumental metamorphosis all around them. George remembers that Las Vegas had only two hotels when he first got to town in 1945. At the corner of Sahara and the Strip was the El Rancho Vegas; he recalls that burning in the mid-1950s in a spectacular fire. There was also the Last Frontier Hotel, which was a little further out, where the Frontier Hotel is today.

George recalls that the Kiwanis Club—which he would belong to for more than fifty years, including a term as president—met at the Last Frontier Hotel, across the street from the Desert Inn. He says he re-members watching the Desert Inn sit there and sit there for about a year or two, and being very delighted when it finally got finished. He recalls that back in the '40s and '50s they could go out to any of the hotels and see a show almost for the price of drinks.

"The Last Frontier was by far our favorite," remembers George. "It had a great bar and the Ramona Room had great shows. It really was a very attractive place for all the local people to go to. The Flamingo came in, I think it was 1947. Bugsy Siegel got shot because it greatly overran its cost and the mob got rid of him," George explains.

The Desert Inn, the Flamingo, and various others were rumored to be built with mob money from Cleveland and other cities, says George. "In the old days, during prohibition, they earned huge amounts in the liquor trade, which was, of course, illegal. But they branched out to a lot of other things, like Al Capone in Chicago. But overall, here they were very community-minded and they joined community organizations and spon-sored community events."

George makes the comment that he sees a lot of allegations in the press about mob activity—but how true they are, he doesn't know. He states, "We had people here in the '40s and '50s from a number of different cities who were in the various mobs, but I think they kept their noses clean here. Most of the mob has been discontinued here simply because there are private corporations now, and it's very difficult to have ten thousand stockholders and do shenanigans. Of course, the state gaming commission has been excellent in policing the gaming."

Some longtime Las Vegas residents have said that the mob did a better job of running things than the way they are run now, and George agrees.

"We liked it much better. There's no question. The hotel owners wanted to keep crime at a minimum, and their licenses depended upon it; as a consequence, the locals that had been here for awhile enjoyed the facilities of the various hotels and we knew a great many of the people who ran them, through Kiwanis or other service groups. As far as we were concerned, it was much more friendly than the current way of running hotels. There was less crime in those days."

With the increased buildup of downtown Las Vegas and its outlying areas, the physician numbers gradually increased. As George observes, "In the last ten years it's just gone hog wild. The population here has blossomed so hugely that the number of doctors here now is a far cry from what it used to be."

By the early '60s, as the city's landscape continued to change, something else in medicine began to change also. Dorothy George recalls a conversation she had as a member of the medical auxiliary's nursing scholarship committee, while attending a meeting of the nursing staff at the University of Nevada, Las Vegas. "I asked if they were going to teach the student nurses bedside nursing, which was very important to me. I was asked how my day went when I was in nursing and I described it to them. I was told by one of the nursing professors, 'We don't teach our nurses to be slaves.' That really shocked me—and it hurt, because to me, nurses are supposed to be there to take care of patients, to be compassionate and helpful and help them recover more quickly," says Dorothy.

The nursing profession today is vastly different from those years when Dorothy worked as a nurse at Clark County General and in her husband's office. "Nurses don't do bedside nursing anymore—mostly the R.N.s do the bookwork, the paperwork, except in specialty units such as intensive care or recovery," Dorothy maintains. Recently she had a friend who was in the hospital for six days following major surgery; her friend didn't have a change of bed linen the whole time, says Dorothy.

"To me, hospitals would profit more if the patients have a good rapport with the hospital—and patients would recuperate faster," she adds.

Dorothy says that while she enjoyed her nursing career during the years she worked, and was proud to say she was an R.N., unfortunately, that is no longer true.

"It's my understanding that nurses today are trained to be head nurses, teachers, and to work in intensive care and the operating room. The floor duty is done mostly by aides and LPNs (licensed practical nurses)," Dorothy says. She explains that the registered nurses who used to do bedside nursing would look for problems, illnesses, and complications that somebody who's not trained doesn't know how to look for today. Dorothy remembers that when she was in nursing, when doctors made rounds they would ask the nurses about the patients' symptoms— and they relied more on the floor nurses' observations than those of the head nurse.

"Florence Nightingale would turn over in her grave if she knew what was happening in her chosen field today!" Dorothy asserts. (Florence Nightingale was an English nurse of the nineteenth century, whose tireless service, at night as well as during the day, made her a symbol for all nursing and for any kind of dedicated service.)

"Her whole philosophy was toward bedside nursing and helping patients to be comfortable and heal faster," explains Dorothy.

Through Dr. George's forty-two years in practice in Las Vegas, he continued to distinguish himself through service to mankind through medicine. In 1969 he received the Nevada State Medical Association's Outstanding Community Service Award. From 1971 to 1973 he was a rating examiner for the Nevada Industrial Commission, and from 1973 to 1988 served as medical advisor to the State Industrial Insurance System. The Jean Hanna Clark Rehabilitation Center, part of that system, rehabilitated workers who were injured on the job and privately as well; from 1979 to 1982, George was the Center's medical director.

"The Jean Hanna Clark Rehabilitation Center was instituted under Governor Mike O'Callaghan and named after his deceased valuable secretary," notes George. In recognition of George's work there, he was presented with Nevada's Living Treasure in Rehabilitation Award in 1983 by then-Governor Richard Bryan and the Governor's Committee on Employment of the Handicapped.

George also became involved with the newly-established School of Medicine at the University of Nevada, Reno (UNR) campus. The medical school prepares students to be physicians through its clinical programs and rotations. George, as president of the Nevada State Medical Association in 1966, was affiliated with the school in its early stages of development.

"We did support through the legislature and with lobbying to support the start of a medical school in Nevada," George recalls. Starting in 1972, he spent five years on the school's Selections Committee. In 1995, the school honored George with its *Praeceptor Carissimus* Award; given by the Dean at graduation, the award honors a physician considered to be the ideal role model.

The status of many Las Vegas hospitals also changed over the years. The main hospital with which George was affiliated, Clark County General Hospital, was renamed Southern Nevada Memorial Hospital in 1956; since 1986 it has been known as University Medical Center of Southern Nevada, in keeping with its role as the teaching hospital for the University of Nevada School of Medicine in Las Vegas. With medical technology advances came shifts in thinking on patient care, so that patients recovering from surgery began spending less and less time in the hospital. Whereas as recently as the early 1960s, post-surgical patients were routinely hospitalized for up to ten days, the modern trend is to keep patients in the hospital for a few days at most. The declining number of hospital inpatient beds required had an effect on virtually every Las Vegas hospital. In 1974, the Las Vegas Hospital and Clinic, originally Las Vegas' main hospital, closed. Over the years, new hospitals opened, and existing ones diversified their services in order to stay afloat in the environment of reduced hospital stays.

By 1988, the year that marked George's forty-eighth year in practice, he knew he wanted to retire. There were other things he wanted to do.

Ready for Retirement After Nearly
Fifty Years as a Doctor

1988–1999

LAS VEGAS, NEVADA

Reflecting on his decision to retire, George says, "Time has a way of going by and I retired when I hit seventy-five—I figured that was enough. I decided that I would hang it up for the most part, although I still see some of my old-time patients."

He still has his active medical license and still sees patients he had in the 1940s and 1950s, he says. "I still make house calls on old-time patients of mine, and the bond that you build by long relationships that way is a huge asset."

The long-term relationship he embarked on with Dorothy nearly five decades ago has developed into a mutual admiration society. Ask him to name his greatest joys, either in his practice or in his personal life, and he looks warmly across the room at Dorothy.

"My greatest joy is sitting on the couch there," George answers with a big smile. Dorothy beams back. He continues, saying, "After forty-nine years—plus."

In 1999, with his wife by his side, George turned eighty-six. He says that they have been very happy in Las Vegas.

"In more recent years we haven't been real happy about the tremendous population growth, but we've always thoroughly enjoyed this area. This has always been a very friendly town. I joined the Kiwanis Club here in 1946, I joined the V.F.W. here in 1946, the American Legion and the Elks, and I've kept up my association and membership in all of those. We just enjoy so many people that we've known. Over the years we've had such excellent friends here that we've known for many, many years; unfortunately, some of our friends are dying off these days because of the passage of years. But we enjoy the climate, we enjoy the town. But, as I say, we liked it when it was a little bit smaller," says George.

He points to the ripple effect generated by the opening of the large casinos, such as when the MGM opened, with 8,000 new employees. "But you have 8,000 families, then you have the TV people who have to fix their TVs, the food stores that have to do the food—so it just spreads rapidly," George says. "That's just that one hotel: it jumped things hugely."

Today, George spends his time doing the things he's wanted to do for awhile, things he says he couldn't do as actively when he was practicing medicine. In 1998, for instance, he traveled to Baltimore to attend his medical class' sixtieth reunion; he says thirteen of the alumni showed up. He also spends much of his time working for the community, especially in the area of charity work.

George became a Catholic after marrying Dorothy. "I've been a member of the Catholic church for many years. But there's no conflict. When I go back to visit my brother, who still lives in Sudlersville, I really respect their religion as well," says George. The church they belong to, Our Lady of Las Vegas Catholic Church, has been most important to them, says George. Dorothy works in the church office, and he and Dorothy regularly volunteer and make lunches for sobered-up alcoholics or drifters who are hired out for work for the day; the church is trying to get these people organized into a more stable lifestyle, George explains.

"I had a lot of other things in the Kiwanis and the Veterans of Foreign Wars and other organizations like the Knights of Columbus that I wanted to do," George adds. He is a life member of the American Legion, the Elks Lodge 1468, and the American Academy of Family Physicians. His chosen service organization has been the Kiwanis Club, since joining more than fifty years ago; in 1968 he was president of the Uptown Las Vegas Kiwanis Club, and in 1998 he received the Hixson Award from Kiwanis International. His service work is extremely important to him, and he says he has strongly urged doctors over the years to become actively involved with service work in their communities ("We owe it to our people to help out other than in medicine").

George says his biggest hobby is gardening. He states proudly, "I still take care of cutting my grass and all my yard work. I still take care of my own pool and so forth, because I think the activity is good for you. That's been my biggest hobby, but as I say, I do a lot of work for the church, with the Kiwanis Club, with the Veterans of Foreign Wars and what not—and I enjoy all of them."

He has been married to Dorothy for nearly fifty years now. All told they have six children, four from his previous marriage and the two daughters they adopted. Of those two, Janelle is a school teacher in Las Vegas at Lewis E. Rowe School, says George, and June is a general surgeon and colo-rectal surgeon in California.

"She's board certified in both, and practices over in Oakland, California at Kaiser Hospital," George says proudly.

His children from his former marriage include Margaret Quimby, the oldest, a registered nurse, and the second oldest, Patricia Meyers, a former licensed vocational nurse, both in Maryland. Joseph M. George III, the third oldest, lives in Georgia and is sales manager for a banking computer software firm. Lyn, the youngest, works for the city of Waco, Texas.

"We, ourselves, have two children, but we have a great relationship with all six children and their families. We have got twenty-five grandchildren, eighteen great-grandchildren, and three great-great-grandchildren," notes George. "That's what you get from having daughters first, and they have daughters first, and so forth."

Asked to give advice to doctors practicing today, George offers some succinct words of inspiration, drawn no doubt from his old-fashioned upbringing by a close family in that small town of Sudlersville many years ago—and from nearly fifty years of experience as a twentieth-century healer in the traditional yet ultramodern megalopolis of Las Vegas.

"I think my most important advice to doctors practicing now would be: be ethical. I think that is the basic key of everything," George maintains.

"If you're not ethical, I don't care if you're the world's best doctor. You're going to cause more trouble than you're going to help."

3

James Daniel Barger, M.D.

Pathologist; Years Practiced: 1942–1987

"Committed to quality. That's what he

represented in the minds of everybody:

a symbol who stood for quality."

—Ronald Slaughter, M.D. on

James D. Barger, M.D.

Thinking Outside the Box

1917–1935

BISMARCK, NORTH DAKOTA
WINONA, MINNESOTA
GRAND FORKS, NORTH DAKOTA

On his off days he's been spotted in sweats. He once showed up dressed like a farmer to pick up an important colleague at the airport. People chatting casually with him out on the street or in the grocery store would probably never guess that this soft-spoken, down-to-earth man of few words is a great reader. But his home is filled with books: they take up all the book shelves and line nearly every corner of the house, sitting in neat stacks on the floors below the shelves. They bear witness to his penchant for the knowledge to be found in the printed word, just one hidden facet of this man's deceptively simple appearance.

Another aspect of his complex personality is that this distinguished pathologist, James Daniel Barger, M.D., played a crucial role in ushering a young city out of the frontier era. He helped to plant Las Vegas squarely in the twentieth century, enabling it to stand up to scrutiny as a well-respected, highly specialized medical community. Because he possessed the leadership qualities and intuitive ability to navigate through the disparate worlds inhabited by doctors and by the government, Dr. Barger was able to bring those sometimes strange bedfellows together to cooperate on one common ideal: the standardization for inspection and accreditation of physicians' office laboratories. As a spokesman for laboratory quality and high standards in medical practice in general, he put himself on the line.

Some would call it having vision, while others might label him a progressive thinker; modern-day observers would describe it as thinking outside the box. But it is probably Barger himself who puts it best, as he reminisces about his childhood and the type of person he has become.

"I was always curious," Barger says with his genial smile, giving a simple and characteristically modest explanation for his success. "I never did things the way they were supposed to be done."

That innate sense of curiosity, combined with his pure nerve ("more guts than brains," as Barger likes to say), landed his name in a dozen editions of *Who's Who* as well as in other international biographies of prominent figures. Yet his entrance into the world was ordinary and unremarkable, giving no hint of the auspicious debut he would one day make in the complex world of national medical politics.

He was born on May 17, 1917, at Saint Alexis Hospital in Bismarck, North Dakota. His father, Michael Thomas Barger, had worked in the grain business in his home town of St. Peter, near Minneapolis in Minnesota, before coming to North Dakota. It was there Michael met the Wisconsin woman he would later marry, Mary Margaret Donohue, who was also working in Minneapolis. After their marriage in 1904, the two settled in a little town near Bismarck, where Michael began working as a country banker. They had their first child, Thomas, in 1909, and James was born eight years later.

Signs that Jim Barger was an unusual child who would go on to do things his own way appeared early in his life. In grade school at Linton, North Dakota, he was a year ahead of his class, he says, having skipped the first grade altogether.

"My mother taught me at home so when I got to first grade, I'd know all that stuff," he recalls. "I was too smart a kid, I guess, my brother and I." Although his mother was not a professional educator ("she was just an Irish lady," Barger says), she did possess the uncommon foresight to recognize her sons' intelligence when they were still very young. She believed that her home schooling could best prepare the boys for school.

By the time he turned sixteen, the youngest Barger boy had grown into a young man who was constantly tinkering with chemistry experiments. He purchased some of his equipment and made whatever he could not buy. That passion for experimentation that began when he was in high school would continue throughout his life.

After graduating from high school in 1934, Barger followed in his older brother's footsteps and enrolled at Saint Mary's College, now Saint Mary's University, in Winona, located in southern Minnesota. During his two years there, the strapping young North Dakotan with the thick, wavy hair was on the school's track team. It was there he developed his passion for running, a sport he would enjoy for most of his life. His coach at St. Mary's was "Moose" Krause, a famous Notre Dame football and basketball player. With Krause, Barger got to go up to Minneapolis to participate in the indoor track meet for the Minnesota College Conference. He recalls the big fuss a local newspaperman attempted to make there over Krause.

"We arrived, the newspaper man who was driving the car, myself, and Moose Krause, at Red Wing, Minnesota, at the top of the main street just at noon. In those days, at noon, the Farm and Home Hour came on with a rousing Sousa march. So they rolled the windows down, turned up the radio full-blast, and drove down the main street of this town in Minnesota, the driver saying, 'Here he is, folks, the All-American from Notre Dame, Ed "Moose" Krause!' Krause was waving to the crowd, who was wondering, 'What's going on?'"

Barger, who says he got to know Krause pretty well, likes to tell an anecdote about how Krause, a natural athlete, took to tennis immediately.

"I went into his office one morning. His assistant is there and he is reading to him. I said, 'What are you doing?' He said his assistant got a new tennis racket, so they borrowed one for Moose. His assistant is reading him the rules. I said to him, 'Have you ever played tennis before?' He said, 'No, but he's reading me the rules.' After lunch time I went out. They were playing. I don't know how long they had been playing, but Ed 'Moose' is saying to his opposite, 'Isn't it about time you won a game?' Never played before, of course," Barger notes with a chuckle.

The following year, 1935, Barger transferred to the University of North Dakota in Grand Forks. He remembers that he was thinking he wanted to become a clinical chemist. In undergraduate school, the free thinker with the typically curious mind set continued to experiment by himself. Barger recalls that he was doing "kind of crazy research work on my own," as he puts it, including a great deal of work on alkaline phosphatase.

"Why Just Don't You Just Try Premed?"

1935–1939

By the time he was halfway through his University courses, Barger had decided he wanted to become a chemical engineer. But his mother spoke up: in typical fashion, she had something else in mind for her son.

"You've got to understand that Jewish families and Irish families are much the same," explains Barger. "In Jewish families and Irish families, the firstborn is clergy, either a rabbi or a priest. My brother was not going to be a priest, nor was I. After that, you come down this list and the next one is a doctor. Then lower down on the list is a lawyer. So my brother, who was eight years older than I, went off to St. Mary's then transferred to North Dakota. When he went to North Dakota, he was told to do two things: one, he was not to join a fraternity, and two, he was to enroll in premed.

"He had been there less than a week and he joined the Kappa Sigma fraternity and enrolled in the mining engineering school. But of course he went on to do pretty good—he ended up as president and chairman of the board of a great big oil company, toured Saudi Arabia and a few other things," Barger says wryly.

Barger remembers how his mother attempted to dissuade him from his original career choice with a pointed suggestion: "Why don't you just try premed?"

Barger laughs at the memory. "Of course, I couldn't very well just try it. Once I was there, I was caught, because there was no other way to go. I was committed to medicine."

In those years, North Dakota was one of a number of two-year medical schools which gave students the basic sciences; the students would then transfer to complete their last two clinical years. Other two-year schools Barger remembers included South Dakota, Utah, Creighton, and Tulane. The tuition charged by the two-year school at North Dakota was a nominal amount, he remembers.

As a young medical student during the 1930s, Barger ran into some colorful characters, including the dean of the medical school, whom he describes as a meticulous fellow who would get into arguments about anatomy. In those days, before there was widespread knowledge of the harmful effects of tobacco, the practice of chewing tobacco was commonplace. Barger remembers that both the dean of the medical school and the dean of the mining engineering school chewed cut plug.

"The dean of the mining engineering school took the drawer of the upper right hand desk and put sand in it, so he could just pull the drawer out and spit in the sand," recalls Barger. "But the dean of the medical school kept it in his mouth, behind the cheek. There was a spittoon on the way out of class. He would come out and he would do a little curtsy and drop his tobacco in the spittoon going by. It was really quite interesting."

While Barger was at the university, he began dating a young woman he would later describe as the love of his life, Janie Ray Regan. The two kept up a steady correspondence, even after his graduation from the university in 1939. Upon graduation, he was awarded two degrees—a bachelor of arts degree in liberal arts (chemistry) as well as a bachelor of science degree in medicine and chemistry.

He remembers being accepted at Northwestern to begin his medical education and not going; then he was accepted there again to transfer, but didn't go. He decided instead to attend the University of Pennsylvania in Philadelphia, he says, mainly because Penn was the oldest medical school. (The University of Pennsylvania had also been attended by another Las Vegas physician, Dr. Joseph George, Jr. [see Part Two, previous biography in this book]. Dr. George, a family practitioner, had earned his bachelor of arts degree at the university in 1934, five years before Barger would attend.)

$580.00 a Year for Medical School, Tough Monkeys, and the Army

1939–1944

PHILADELPHIA, PENNSYLVANIA
ROCHESTER, MINNESOTA
MILWAUKEE, WISCONSIN
WASHINGTON, D.C.

The tuition charged in those days by Penn was $580 a year, Barger remembers. That amount seems miniscule when compared to contemporary tuition costs: in 1999, $8,500 is the yearly tuition for out-of-state students attending the University of Nevada, and tuition is more than $30,000 for a private school. Yet back in 1939, although the $580 charged by Penn was considered a lot of money, Barger's father was able to pay it. He had managed to save enough to put both his sons through school.

The same year, thousands of miles away from North Dakota, a terrible conflict between Germany and Great Britain was gathering force. Barger will never forget what happened the day he left for medical school at Penn.

"I woke up September 3, 1939, and as my father woke up in the morning he always played the radio at full blast," Barger recalls. He tells the rest of the story with a British accent: "I woke up this morning and heard Chamberlain say, 'We have asked the Germans, and we have not received an answer, and we are now at WAH!' That day my father took me to Bismarck and I caught the train to Philadelphia to complete my medical education. Effectively I left home on the third of September, 1939."

At Penn, recalls Barger, there were some wonderful people. "They had Dr. O.V. Batson in anatomy, who was a 'wild man.' Then Eldridge Eliason was a surgeon, a very meticulous man. I remember one time when I was to scrub with him. I got my scrub suit and my shoes on but I didn't have socks. He said, 'I always like to have my people look neat,' and he gave me a pair of his socks to wear so I would look neat."

In his third year, Barger was taught by Dr. John Stokes, whom Barger describes as being a very good writer. Syphilis was quite a plague at that time, recalls Barger, and Stokes had written a book called *Modern Clini-*

cal Syphilology. Barger recalls that Stokes liked to keep things hopping in his class, and likens the atmosphere to a three-ring circus at times.

"Every Thursday, when we were in the third year, he'd come in and there would be three or four patients on gurneys in the 'pit.' Dr. Stokes would be in the middle with his lectern. Everybody sat in their assigned seats and then he would assign two students for each of these patients there. Their job was, in one hour, to get all of the history, physical findings, and everything so they could present them to the class the next hour. In the meantime, the class was divided. Each quarter of the class would come down and spend fifteen minutes going through the pits, seeing these patients," explains Barger.

"Well, the poor guys down there were trying to get the findings on these patients, and then at the end of that time he would move to the center and they'd wheel one patient out. Then the two poor guys that spent that first hour examining the patient were really put on the hot seat."

In the summer between his third and fourth years, Barger spent time as an observer at the Mayo Foundation Clinic in Rochester, Minnesota. He recalls two groups, one at Saint Mary's Hospital and a smaller group downtown at the Methodist Hospital. About eight or nine students got to spend the summer with Dr. A.C. Broders, a pathologist with whom Barger became very good friends. Years later, Barger would return to visit Dr. Broders, whom he describes as a wonderful man. Broders' office was located on the top of the Methodist Hospital.

"Broders was quite a hunter—or thought so, anyway," recalls Barger. "In fact, his son told me he had the most expensive Victrola (RCA Victor's brand of phonograph, or record player) you could get. You didn't have sound systems in those days, and the main records he had on were duck calls. He would play these and practice the calls."

Barger became an M.D. in 1941, but didn't get to go to his graduation from Penn; he was starting his internship at Milwaukee County Hospital, where all the tours began on the 15th of June rather than on the first day of July. (Longtime general practitioner Dr. Gerald Joseph Sylvain had also completed his internship at Milwaukee County Hospital several years earlier, in 1933, before practicing in Las Vegas from 1942 to 1994 [see Part One, the first biography in this book.])

By the time Barger completed his internship in 1942, he had become fascinated with the study of disease (pathology). Because of this, and because of the variety inherent in that specialty, he decided he wanted to become a pathologist, a physician specializing in the study of disease processes with the aim of understanding their nature and causes. He would achieve that by observing samples of blood, urine, feces, and diseased tissue from living patients or at autopsy; by X-ray; or by other techniques. But that meant more than just working in the laboratory, Barger emphasizes.

"To be a pathologist, you must have at least a knowledge of clinical medicine, otherwise it doesn't work. Maybe you're not one who's going into therapeutics and treating it, but you have a knowledge of clinical medicine."

At the time Barger decided on his specialty, World War II was nearing its peak. He was drafted into the Army of the United States (A.U.S.), not the United States Army, which he calls "the regular army. The Army of the United States was for all us draftees," he explains.

His first assignment was to report to Denver, Colorado, to Fitzsimmons General Hospital. While at Fitzsimmons, which he calls the Fitz, Barger became good friends with Dr. Philip Levine. Dr. Levine and others had made anti-Rh serum, and Drs. Barger and Levine became interested in the Rh factor, explains Barger.

"I got in on the Rh factor very early. I was trying to make an Rh serum. Supposedly you could inject rhesus monkey blood into guinea pigs: that's the way they made the anti-Rh serum. Of course, afterwards, you got it from people who made it because they were Rh-negative and got Rh-positive blood," says Barger.

At this point Barger's work ran into a problem he solved in his own unconventional fashion. "I needed some rhesus monkey blood. The tuberculosis hospital in Denver is run by a church group. It's a good hospital. They had monkeys. I went over and looked at those rhesus monkeys. They were almost as big as me, and boy, they were tough. So I decided that was not for me. Then I went to the zoo. The zoo keeper very nicely got me the rhesus monkeys' blood," says Barger, laughing.

Upon returning to the hospital, Barger met his commanding officer, who asked where he had been. Barger replied, "To the zoo, sir." His C.O. said, "What for?" Barger answered, "To get some rhesus monkey blood, sir." The C.O. demanded, "What for?" Barger responded with, "To make some Rh antibody, sir," at which his commanding officer just smiled and walked away.

From the Fitz Barger was transferred to Washington D.C., for the opening of the general dispensary in the Pentagon. "I was there to open that—it was right at the end of the concourse. I was there until '44. It was great duty at the dispensary," recalls Barger.

They had a saying there, Barger remembers. "We said we never looked twice at anybody in there unless they had three stars or no stripes."

He says they saw a lot of interesting people there, and remembers one in particular. "We had one guy that came in that had a blood sugar of 700 and was fine. He had been a prisoner of war in the Philippines and had escaped, and here he was with this horrendous blood sugar level." (Blood sugar is the concentration of glucose in the blood; the normal range is between 70 and 110 mg/100 cc.)

All during those years, Barger says, he had kept up his correspondence with Janie Ray Regan. But after Barger was sent to Washington, she married a man in Colorado. In 1944, another transfer came through for young Dr. Barger: he was sent by the Office of American Affairs to Bolivia.

Rationed Penicillin in the Amazon Basin

1944–1945

RIBERALTA, BOLIVIA

During the fourteen months Barger spent as a pathologist in the little eastern Bolivia jungle town of Riberalta, he recalls going every place and seeing a side of medicine he would never have seen in the States. It was there he met Sister Mercy of the MaryKnolls, whom he describes as being very nice. A physician, Sister Mercy was the sister of Dr. John Hirschbeck, the dean of Marquette University.

With a war raging, many essentials were in short supply, including penicillin; Barger recalls that to get penicillin you had to be on the list. Sister Mercy got some penicillin and asked him to guard it for her while she was gone temporarily. At the same time, there was a German surgeon there who had sent for penicillin for a patient on whom he had operated that morning.

"I was sitting around the bishop's house one night when the surgeon sends over word that he needs to have penicillin," Barger recalls.

Barger realized the patient had been operated on in the hot and humid tropical weather, and suspected the patient's real problem was that she was dehydrated. Barger decided he'd better go over to the hospital to take a look at the patient. It was exactly as he thought: she was dehydrated. He said to the surgeon, "She doesn't need penicillin. What she needs is fluid and blood."

Barger decided they would transfuse the patient; as he puts it, "Sometimes you have got more guts than brains, as they say." He drew some blood from her and took it back to their office, where they had sort of a small lab.

As Barger explains, the patient was related to the chief of police. Barger describes the chief as a guy who had been promoted as the result of having been on the winning side in a nasty little war between Bolivia and Paraguay.

"But he had been a very un-nice guy," says Barger. "He gave hot water enemas to the opposition to the revolution as punishment for the rebels' campaign against the government—so they banished him up there."

Barger had blood from the chief and from the patient plus some other blood, and he crossmatched by mixing them to see which one would mix smoothly and not coagulate, or clump.

"After we determined who would crossmatch, we used a 50 cc syringe. The chief just put his arms out. We did multiple punctures to finally get about 300 cc of blood. Then at midnight, and I remember this well, we go walking through the grass streets of this town, with our blood and one of the priests who was with me. We go over to the hospital and run the blood into the patient. She perks up quite a bit."

The next morning, Barger had a meeting with the surgeon, who was complaining. He was saying, "I do not understand what you have done with his patient. You have killed her!"

Barger tried to explain that they had given her a blood transfusion and she was much better, but the surgeon kept going on about how they had probably killed her. Barger says the chief of police finally told the surgeon, "If she dies, I will kill you." The surgeon turned white and walked away, Barger recalls.

That was in 1944. Barger remembers also that he was told that beriberi, a nutritional disorder caused by deficiency of vitamin B1 (thiamin), had supposedly been reported there years earlier, between 1915 and 1920. When Barger was there, of course, the disease had practically been eradicated. But, ever curious, he went out looking for where they had reported beriberi. It was always "a little bit farther on," he says, but he kept searching. He finally got to a place that was yet a little farther on, at which point he stopped.

"It was in the midst of the Amazon jungle, and I said, 'The beriberi—it can just stay there.'"

Barger was still stationed in Bolivia when the war ended in 1945. Like most survivors of World War II, he can pinpoint exactly where he was when the Allies announced victory. He had just taken an Air Force pilot who was assigned to the U.S. air mission in Bolivia to have an upper GI (gastrointestinal [stomach and small intestines]) series X-ray, and had made a diagnosis of gastric ulcer. After that, they came down the hill and stopped in their favorite restaurant, which was run by a bunch of German refugees. The radio was blaring when the news came through that the war was over in Europe. It was V-E Day, the day the German armies surrendered and the Allies declared victory in Europe. Barger remembers how the cooks and waitresses all poured out of the kitchen.

"They broke out the champagne and we had quite a celebration that afternoon—got a little drunk," remembers Barger.

On V-J Day, when the Japanese army surrendered and the Allies declared victory over Japan, Barger had gone across the mountains to a little town in the Amazon Basin. He can't remember exactly what he was looking for, but he says he was after something. That night they had the radio on from Montevideo when they got the news.

"MacArthur had signed the peace declaration. We had a siren which we blew. We came out and the people gathered around. We said, 'Esta la fin del guerre! Esta la fin del guerre!' We broke out a few more bottles of beer, and that was the way we ended that war."

Army Transfers, Marriage, and
Mayo Postgraduate Work

1945–1949

DOUGLAS, ARIZONA
DENVER, COLORADO
WASHINGTON, D.C.
ROCHESTER, MINNESOTA

The young doctor, just twenty-eight years old, emerged from the Bolivian jungle sporting a mustache and full beard, having gone his entire tour of duty in Bolivia without shaving. He recalls that when he came down and had his pictures taken, a colonel with the U.S. military mission jumped up and down at the sight of the shaggy doctor. But the colonel's reaction didn't faze Barger, he says, because he was planning to shave it off anyway. During those years Barger also enjoyed smoking a pipe, a practice he later gave up, he says.

After returning from Bolivia, Barger married a nurse named Susie Belle Helm. She had been commissioned in the United States Army Nurse Corps as either a captain or a major, says Barger. They were married in Douglas, Arizona, in 1945. By that time, practically on his way out of the service, Barger spent a little bit of time again at the Fitz in Denver. Then his final army transfer sent him back to Washington, D.C.

In April 1946, he returned to the Mayo Foundation at the University of Minnesota to start postgraduate work on his masters degree in pathology. At the Mayo Clinic, Barger recalls, he had a little corner of the laboratory where he was able to work on his interests. He remembers the head of the lab, Dr. Edward C. Kendall ("a nice guy," as described by Barger). Dr. Kendall would go on to win the Nobel Prize in 1950 for his work with cortisone.

Barger remembers doing some work around 1948 on Schiff reagent, a stain for nucleic acid of nuclei. "They came out with the LE cell, lupus erythematosus, and showed that people with this disease would get inclusions in a certain type of leukocyte. The inclusions were the nuclei of lymphocytes. They had to show that this was nucleic acid or nuclear material in these inclusions. The histochemical stain to demonstrate that this was nuclear material (nucleic acid) was the use of the Schiff reagent which was specific for DNA in tissues (cells)," explains Barger. He says this demonstration was necessary to prove their hypothesis.

Since Barger knew exactly how to do Schiff's reagent stains, some students asked if he would do it for them. He said he wouldn't do it for them, but could show them how to do it. As he describes it, it was a simple technique. "It certainly wasn't hard to do. You had to put the slide into hydrochloric acid. You left it in there for an hour or so. Then you took it out of the Schiff reagent, washed it, completed the staining procedure, and mounted it for examination. It was not a very complicated procedure."

Then, as Barger recalls, "Saturday morning, about ten o'clock, this fellow appears with this slide. I said, 'Okay, fine. you put it in this solution and leave it in there for an hour and then I'll tell you what to do.' I'm getting ready to go home around a quarter to twelve or so; the slide is still there, but he's not there. So, finally, what the heck, I'll just finish it off and stain it. In a couple of days he comes wandering back and says, 'By the way, whatever happened to that slide?' I said, 'I stained it. Whatever happened to you?' 'Oh, he said, we went up to the football game in Minneapolis.' I said, 'Great!'"

Barger points out that from that one slide, the students wrote a definitive article about the LE cell phenomenon. Although he remembers that he laughed about it for a long time, this would not be the first such scenario in Barger's life. There would be many times to come when, because of his hard work, others would accomplish their goals. Yet, if truth be told, it was the quietly brilliant man behind the scenes who made those accomplishments possible—without taking the credit.

Barger says at that time he was still working out methods with alkaline phosphatase, an enzyme sometimes described as being pretty ubiquitous in the human body. Working on alkaline phosphatase and bone healing, Barger was able to demonstrate the enzyme in decalcified bone sections, which, he remembers, required a little doing. "If you decalcify the bone, you destroy the enzyme with the usual methods. But I worked out a method you could use to do it. Five or six guys came to me and I was able to do the phosphatases, low man on the totem pole. The orthopedic surgeons developed an exhibit on alkaline phosphatase in bone healing, which they took to a national meeting. It won first place. I was the provider of examples demonstrating the enzyme in the histologic preparations," notes Barger, adding, "For this, I was put on the exhibit as the last author."

Barger says that because of the recognition at the national orthopedic meeting, the exhibit was also sent to the American Medical Association (AMA) meeting in Chicago. In those days, he recalls, the AMA had exhibits at the meeting, so he was invited to accompany it.

As a postgraduate fellow at the Mayo Foundation, Barger was able to spend time with his good friend, Dr. Broders. At one of the Broders' Christmas parties, Barger got his first taste of what his chosen specialty held in store for him.

"They would have a receiving line and Mrs. Broders would greet everybody. To the wives of the various fellows she'd say, 'Oh, Mrs. Smith, your husband is in surgery. Oh, isn't that wonderful and I'm certainly glad to know.' The thing that got Mrs. Broders was she lived in the 'hill.' The other clinicians lived up there too, and grateful patients would give them gifts."

But, because Dr. Broders was a pathologist, points out Barger, he didn't have grateful patients. So his wife would be very solicitous of the young ladies who had married the pathologists. "To the surgeons' wives she'd say, 'My dear, wonderful! Albert's a pathologist and he didn't get these things,' and she would carry on about it," remembers Barger. But rather than show resentment about the fact that the work performed made by pathologists often goes unrecognized, Barger amiably observes, "It was really funny."

A Taste of Politics

1949–1964

After receiving his masters in pathology in 1949, Barger took a job in Tucson, Arizona as pathologist for Pima County Hospital. By that time, there were two additions to the Barger family: James D. Barger Jr., born in 1948, and Mary Susan Barger, born in 1949. In Tucson, Barger was also doing consulting work at the Veterans Administration Hospital. But he soon tired of going back and forth between the two hospitals, which were on opposite sides of town.

Barger relocated in 1950, moving to Phoenix to become the pathologist at Maricopa County Hospital. A year later, in 1951, he took a job as chairman of the pathology department at Phoenix' Good Samaritan Hospital, a position he would hold for thirteen years. With his military obligations behind him, he was finally able to stay in one place and raise a family. But just as the thirty-four year-old pathologist was settling down and enjoying newfound success in his professional life, his wife, Susie, an asthmatic, died a pulmonary death. Their son and daughter were just three and two years old, respectively.

He met a woman who would take over as mother to young James Jr. and Mary Susan. In 1952, Josephine Steiner became Barger's second wife. Barger has great praise for the woman and the role she played in his life.

"She really was a great lady—very capable," Barger says. "She had her masters of science in nursing and had graduated from Yale. When Susie died and I was left with two little kids, Josephine more or less took over. It was exactly that."

The family continued to grow: in 1953, Michael Thomas II was born, followed by Mary Elizabeth (nicknamed "Tutubet"), in 1954. Barger's career continued to progress: he became a consultant to several medical facilities, including the Arizona State Tuberculosis Sanatorium and the state mental hospital. During the years he spent in Phoenix, he served as assistant medical examiner for Maricopa County, chairman of the board of the Arizona Tumor Tissue Registry, and chairman of the Arizona Colloquium in Clinical Pathology for the American Society of Clinical Pathologists. He was also the medical director of the Southwest Blood Bank of Arizona from 1951 to 1964, and consultant to the bank's medical director in Scottsdale.

When Barger was working as a pathologist in southern Arizona, the area was much more sparsely populated than it is today. In those days blood would be flown around the southwest. The blood was flown on commercial airlines, Barger says, adding, "I'm pretty sure we didn't have any planes. They developed a pretty good deal. We got it safely to them and I made a lot of good friends," says Barger. Jack Griffith, founder of the Dade County Blood Bank, was one.

The blood bank had been established before Barger became its medical director, he remembers. "The Salt River Valley Blood Bank was started in Tucson, I think, then it went to Phoenix; Quinn Jordan was the manager of the blood bank. He was a man way ahead of his time, because he could see the future. He's the one who started so-called 'blood insurance:' for a certain fee each year, you'd get all the blood transfusions you might need and that kind of service. Quinn was a lawyer, but he was way ahead of his time," notes Barger.

Barger says he then persuaded John Alsever to come out and join the blood banking group. Alsever was very well known at the time in blood banking circles, says Barger.

"I remember one of the things when Quinn and I were in Chicago at the American Medical Association (AMA) meeting. We were there visiting Dr. Leonard Larsen; Leonard Larsen was later president of the AMA, a physician from Bismarck, North Dakota, and I knew him well. Quinn was thinking about blood insurance, and we are about ready to leave. He said to Leonard, 'What would you think if you had some type of insurance-like service where you paid a certain yearly fee—then if you needed blood, you would get whatever you needed for a year, like Blue Cross and Blue Shield?' and Leonard said, 'Well, yeah, that might be okay. What do you think it might cost?' With this, we're going out the door and Quinn says, 'Oh, about $50 a year.' Leonard says 'Well—,' and he was suddenly very, very, interested—but by then we were gone."

Barger says that fifty dollars a year would have been considered a very good price at that time. "We used to say in those days that the best blood was either $500 a unit and then you went down from $500, and you got to $100—it was terrible, bad blood. But then, as one got down further and finally got to the so-called 'free' blood, it was great," recalls Barger.

"This was just an observation of things as they were in the economics of transfusion with private sources. The Red Cross, of course, dealt only in 'free' blood."

While in Phoenix at Good Samaritan, Barger began publishing in such prestigious medical journals as the *American Journal of Clinical Pathology, American Journal of Roentgenology, Radium Therapy and Nuclear Medicine, Arizona Medicine, Transfusion,* and *Veterinary Research.* He would continue to see his articles published for at least another forty years, through 1993.

Barger also began his longstanding practice of holding important offices in professional associations. He served as chairman of the College of American Pathologists, Southwest Regional Committee, from 1953 to 1963. He gained recognition and respect for his tireless work chairing boards, executive committees, and the medical organizations themselves. He held offices in the American Cancer Society, American Society of Clinical Pathologists, American Association of Blood Banks, and the Arizona Society of Pathologists, of which he was president. Barger also served on Blue Shield of Arizona's Professional Committee and the Medicare Adjudication Committee of Arizona.

Around the mid-1950s, Barger expanded his horizons to include the front line of medicine: politics. From 1957 to 1963 he was Arizona Assemblyman for the College of American Pathologists, and from 1958 to 1962 he was a Joint Blood Council board member and American Society of Clinical Pathologists delegate. He was recorder for the College of American Pathologists Assembly from 1963 to 1965. But all of these just served to whet Barger's political appetite. He would go on to immerse himself in the politics of medicine on a national scale—because he was good at it and he enjoyed it.

While in Phoenix, Barger became good friends with Dr. Joe M. Fouts, Jr., also a pathologist at Good Samaritan Hospital. When Fouts left Phoenix in 1958 to take a job as the pathologist for Sunrise Hospital, a new Las Vegas hospital, Barger started thinking about leaving also. Although Barger had established a comfortable career in Phoenix, he was destined to do greater things elsewhere.

A Political Pathologist Raises the Bar

1964–1974

LAS VEGAS, NEVADA

In 1964, Barger left Phoenix and moved with his family to Las Vegas to work with his friend from Phoenix, Joe Fouts, at Sunrise Hospital. The move proved to be a wise choice, for Barger's association with Sunrise Hospital would span a period of twenty-three years. The director of clinical pathology for five years there starting in 1964, Barger was director and chairman of the department of pathology at Sunrise from 1969 to 1980, and was senior pathologist, consultant and quondam chairman from 1980 to 1987. For twenty years, starting in 1965, he was also the medical director of Blood Services in Las Vegas.

Barger was the hospital's second pathologist in the rapidly growing Las Vegas of the 1960s. Just a little more than three decades earlier, in 1927, Las Vegas had consisted of only 2,300 people and was less than one-fifth the size of Reno, which numbered more than 12,000. By 1940, just thirteen years later, the Las Vegas population had quadrupled; the U.S. Census Bureau put the southern Nevada city's population at 8,422 people. The city's phenomenal growth was a direct outgrowth of several monumental events of the 1930s and 1940s.

Gambling, legalized in 1931, became the chief draw. Nevadans learned very well how to profit from the permissive view of the games of chance which traditionally had been seen strictly as a vice. The entire Silver State revolved around the whims of lady luck, which also attracted some of the nation's most notorious racketeers, who channeled hundreds of millions of dollars through the casinos.

The construction of Boulder Dam, later renamed Hoover Dam, also gave the area an unprecedented economic boost in the 1930s. The 726-foot-high dam bordering Arizona and Nevada provided the water and power that guaranteed increased mining activity, luring many to new jobs at mining developments such as Basic Magnesium Incorporated, established in 1942.

With World War II came a wealth of defense-related and military activities. The U.S. Army Air Corps had established the Las Vegas Gunnery School at the site of the old Las Vegas airport; the range was later relocated and expanded as Nellis Air Force Base, which also helped fuel the population explosion. Beginning in 1941, many former GIs (members of the U.S. armed forces) from California and other states flocked to Las Vegas. When the war ended in 1945, more ex-servicemen were freed to become entrepreneurs in the new commercial frontier.

Over the next few decades, Las Vegas became a powerful magnet, attracting those who could afford to enjoy its increasingly grand gaming and resort accommodations. A precious commodity was now everywhere in the arid valley: water forced the tranquil desert into bloom and elegantly designed swimming pools sprang up everywhere. Life was made easier by the invention of air conditioning, which effectively cooled automobile interiors as well as homes, workplaces, and vacation facilities; it also kept the formidable desert heat at bay, all day and night. The city continued its dizzying growth: between 1960 and 1970, the population doubled, expanding from 64,405 to 125,787.

But Las Vegas still had only a handful of hospitals. To accommodate the massive influx of people, Sunrise Hospital opened as a luxury medical center in 1958, catering to wealthy types such as entertainers, gamblers, and well-to-do hotel employees. It was founded by the Adelson brothers and several others, and its financing came from First Western Savings and Loan and the Teamsters Union Pension Fund. Because the Teamsters funded its continuous expansion, Sunrise was sometimes called the Teamsters Hospital. The hospital also developed Nevada's first intensive care unit.

The growing Sunrise Hospital was a sharp contrast to the smaller Phoenix hospital where Barger had begun his career. As he puts it, "Good Samaritan wasn't very big. At Sunrise I could do what I wanted to do."

The first thing he did was to found a pathology group with Fouts; they were joined by pathologist Willis M. Russell, M.D., and the group became Barger and Russell, Ltd., pathology consultants to Sunrise Hospital. Over the years, the group incorporated and continued to expand; today, says Barger, Sunrise Hospital has eleven pathologists. By 1966, just two years after Barger's arrival in Las Vegas, Sunrise was recognized as one of the largest proprietary (owned by investors as a for-profit venture) hospitals west of the Mississippi River.

The Sunrise pathologists were doing clinical pathology with anatomic and some autopsies, more autopsies than they do now, Barger recalls. "Of course, I always say about the younger fellows, there are three reasons that they don't do autopsies. Number one is, 'Well, how am I going to get paid?' and number two is, 'Well, I really don't like to do them,' and number three is—if you really want to know—they don't know how to do them. There are techniques that can make it much simpler, and I learned from a couple of real pros."

The administrator at Sunrise Hospital, the late Nate Adelson, is vividly remembered by Barger, who describes Adelson as one of the fairest and toughest negotiators he's ever seen. Nate Adelson, father of two of the founders, was brought in as the hospital's third administrator; he is credited with putting the hospital on the map.

"There was one thing about Nate: when you reached an agreement and you shook hands on it, that was it. If he made a mistake, he ate it, and if you made a mistake, you ate it—but that was it. A great guy. He's the one who built Sunrise Hospital."

At Southern Nevada Memorial Hospital—originally called Clark County Indigent Hospital, then Clark County General Hospital, and presently known as University Medical Center of Southern Nevada— there was another pathology group, which included Drs. Belliveau, Soloway, and Grayson. Laughing, Barger remembers the time the Grayson group came over to Sunrise to make Nate Adelson a proposition. "They probably wouldn't admit it now, but they did," asserts Barger. Their proposition was simple but straightforward: fire Barger's group and hire them. "But that didn't happen," says Barger, explaining, "Nate was not about to do that."

Barger recalls that it was rumored that Adelson, a businessman from Detroit, had ties with the mob. Barger never had any problems, he says, because he was protected. He observes, with a chuckle, "I was one of his boys."

There was enough work at Sunrise in those days to keep Barger busy. As he puts it, "It was enough to make it interesting, but it wasn't enough so that you were just overwhelmed. " He enjoyed having Bill Russell in the group, even though, says Barger, Russell was cyclothymic, with mood swings up and down ("euphoric at one time and doom the next,"

Barger says). Barger recalls becoming good friends with Dr. Henry Soloway of the Grayson group, even though there was some rivalry between the groups.

In those days, Barger says, Las Vegas was a growing town with a medical group that was not very big. He knew everybody, he says. "We had frequent meetings. You got together and got to know everybody and it was very congenial. I think a lot of that led to consultations and that kind of stuff."

The pathology society, for instance, would have frequent meetings with a dinner, recalls Barger, and the Clark County Medical Society held similar meetings. He says he has always been a member of the medical associations, no matter where he was. "It's just if you're going to a practicing physician, you're a member of the American Medical Association. Most of the doctors in town were."

In the 1970s, Barger became the first physician to join the American Society for Quality Control (ASQC), he says. He describes the organization, now known as ASQ, as an engineers' society. Barger says, "It was a bunch of engineers," then smiles as he continues. "I was in it for a couple of years before I told them I was a physician."

While in the ASQC, Barger recalls that he was working out quality laboratory methods and seeing that they were precise. He says that most of the time, however, he was talking to the wall. His arguments to improve quality often fell on deaf ears.

"Nobody wanted to do it. I remember I was one of the first people to talk about quality in southern California and around here," he asserts.

Over the years, Barger and Russell Ltd. continued to expand and add more pathologists, including Dr. Ronald Slaughter, who joined the group in 1975. Dr. Slaughter, past president of the Nevada State Medical Association and currently a senior pathologist with the group Barger founded (now called Laboratory Medicine Consultants, Ltd.), speaks very highly of the group's founder.

"Jim Barger is a very interesting and fine person. He was very important for the development of medicine in southern Nevada. His influence in our group is still very strong," observes Slaughter. "He provided this town with a really good quality laboratory. He was always a spokesman for labs and standards in medical practice in general."

One important giveaway as to what made Barger tick was the way he treated younger pathologists who were often passed over for partnerships or exploited in other ways by some doctors, notes Slaughter. "Jim was always very concerned with the interests of the younger people he brought into the group. He was a very good mentor, and was very interested in helping his young partners to get into things," Slaughter comments.

Barger's other attributes also helped to build the group, explains Slaughter. "He was a very creative person, extremely well-read. Bob Potter was chief tech of the lab when Sunrise Hospital opened in 1958, and Barger's professional relationship with Potter was extremely important to many of the things Barger accomplished. With Potter excelling at operations, plus Jim's creativity, it became a dynamite partnership."

Barger would become extremely active in the Las Vegas medical community, just as he had in Phoenix. Over the next several decades, he became affiliated with more than thirty professional organizations and held offices in dozens of medical associations. He was secretary-treasurer of the Clark County Medical Society in 1966, president of the Nevada Society of Pathologists from 1967 to 1968, and was governor of the College of American Pathologists (CAP) from 1966 to 1972.

Barger also began writing books: in 1964, his first book, *Medical Terminology, Step by Step*, was published, and *Medical Terminology*, his second book, was published in 1966. He had several more books published over the next few decades, some of which were used in teaching institutions, he says.

Then in 1971, Barger was again left a widower. After nineteen years of marriage, his second wife, Josephine, developed a carcinoma of the lower esophagus. She passed away, leaving him with their two teenage children. Barger, then in his mid-fifties, threw himself into his work and professional activities. He became CAP secretary-treasurer in 1971, vice president, and then president (from 1981 to 1983). Starting in 1974, he volunteered at the University of Nevada School of Medicine in Las Vegas as a clinical associate professor. Barger became a clinical professor at the medical school's department of laboratory medicine and pathology in 1981, and in 1987 achieved the status of professor emeritus.

He began receiving many awards, including the 1971 Blood Services' Community Service Award and the 1975 Sioux Award from the alumni association at his alma mater, the University of North Dakota. In 1977, he was given the College of American Pathologists Scientific Products Award and named Pathologist of the Year by the 7,100 members of CAP. Barger was named Distinguished Physician by the Nevada State Medical Association in 1983 for his contributions to the advancement of the art and science of medicine. He was honored numerous times over the years, as Distinguished Practitioner of Medicine by the National Academies of Practice in 1984 and with the CAP/American Society of Clinical Pathologists Distinguished Service Award in 1985. He received the 1995 Harold L. Feikes Memorial Physician of the Year award, given by the Clark County Medical Society to honor a physician member who has gone beyond the call of duty in serving his or her community. In 1996, Barger was honored with the Nevada State Medical Association President's Award.

During these years, Barger was simultaneously pursuing an interest he had begun to explore earlier in Phoenix, where he had served as an American Society of Clinical Pathologists delegate and as the Arizona Assemblyman for CAP. In Las Vegas he became more and more involved with national politics. At the same time, he continued to take his share of calls and do his share of autopsies, no matter how much time he was devoting to out-of-town travel. His former colleague, Dr. Slaughter, says the other pathologists in his group were happy to support his efforts to advance the standard of quality in the medical community, which also brought some prestige to their group as well.

Bringing Local Medicine into
the Twentieth Century

1974–1987

Barger's political career continued to flourish. With his unpretentious informality, he was a natural for national politics—so much so that he would become a delegate to the AMA (American Medical Association). Some have described him as a good old boy—in the best sense of the expression—because of his relationships with others in his field. Yet while he relished rubbing shoulders with all his buddies at national political meetings, his sense of integrity dictated that he not tolerate pretentiousness in others.

"He was in the middle of things but didn't flaunt it; he loved it," explains Slaughter. Barger's great success in making headway, that ability to get things done, could be attributed to his non-threatening style.

"He was not a soft touch or a pushover, but was genuinely there to help people," Slaughter emphasizes. "He could be big at what he was doing without having to support dragging a big ego behind him. His modesty was genuine, and really refreshing, in a lot of ways: if you're going to find out about him, you'll find out about him slowly. He wouldn't try to bowl you over. He didn't spend a lot of time blowing his own horn."

Working with the CAP (College of American Pathologists) assembly, Barger was able to effect great changes in the way the Las Vegas medical community was perceived. Before 1967, Las Vegas had been regarded by local residents—and also by the rest of the country—as being an area where frontier medicine was the norm, says Slaughter. Among Las Vegans, the general consensus was that if a patient wanted sophisticated, accurate laboratory testing done, or needed to consult a specialist, the patient had better go to California, because Las Vegas was woefully lacking in those services.

Starting in the early 1970s, however, the level of medical quality in the city began to be raised by an influx of specialists, by more sophisticated, state-of-the-art technology, and by hospital improvements. It was Barger who became the recognized leader of that transition.

An example of his leadership can be found in a 1974 letter written by Barger to Las Vegas physician Dr. Jurgens H. Bauer. Barger wrote that many Las Vegans had for years sought medical care outside the community, making the statement that "Many physicians have also obtained laboratory services for their patients outside the community. We propose to make the necessary capital investment in automated instrumentation and staff to provide superior outpatient laboratory services in this community on an economic basis comparable to any other."

By 1975 Las Vegas was at the end of its frontier period and was starting to become a complex medical community, where every specialty would be represented. Barger was one of the leaders at the forefront of this improvement in services. As Slaughter phrases it, "He was committed to quality."

It was Barger who was one of the prime forces and major players behind the program for inspection and accreditation of laboratories—not only in Las Vegas, but on the national level as well. In 1974, he had possessed the foresight to seek the expansion of services at Sunrise Hospital to include outpatient services. With that goal in mind, Barger's group participated in a number of national laboratory improvement programs, earning CAP accreditation.

Barger was able to bring southern Nevada into the arena of twentieth century medicine before the government became involved, by championing the concept of inspection by peers rather than by the government. Slaughter recalls that Barger negotiated with the government and developed strategies for dealing with their regulations; he worked tirelessly and traveled the country for years, always with the goal of promoting better standards for pathologists and physicians.

Barger explains that his effort came about as a result of his realizing a key point, and putting his theory into practice." I decided that what we needed to have was a way to control physician's office laboratories. The pathologists couldn't do this. So I got the internists, family practitioners, and other doctors to appoint some people, and I appointed somebody else. I was kind of in the background all the time. I was just kind of leading along and everything, but when they elected the board, I was not on it," Barger comments. "I just kept in the background all those years, although it was my doing. I never took any credit for it, because I didn't want to."

Barger explains that he believed the physicians' office laboratories needed some supervision. "We did not want them licensed, but we did want them to meet certain standards, and they would be then be accredited by a national organization—the Commission for Office Laboratory Assessment (COLA). I really got that started, but nobody knows I got it started. I got pathologists, surgeons, and internists appointed to the board."

"Actually I'm bragging, but I've often played the behind-the-scenes thing for somebody else," Barger says. It would be accurate to say that when Barger believed something needed to be done, rather than going forward and making a big show out of doing it himself, he was the one who got the people in place to make it happen. He was a true facilitator.

He says with a laugh that he was part of the Bear Cub Patrol, a group of younger pathologists including Drs. Bob Horn, Bill Reals, Larry McCormack, and a few others, all of whom ended up holding high national offices. They were all great friends, says Barger.

"We delighted in introducing what we knew would be controversial issues into the Assembly. We'd get together and we'd write these resolutions. We'd put them in to the Assembly and a lot of times we knew they were inflammatory, but what we did was to make the Assembly a viable institution by making them consider these things. We'd write these things and introduce them, and poor Rudy Schenken, one of the senior statesmen, would spend the whole day going around to all the committees 'saving us from a fate worse than death,' from all these resolutions that were in the Assembly," Barger notes.

Barger gets a big laugh at the memory of the time he met with Schenken one night in New Orleans after one of those sessions. "He had been very, very busy all day, going from committee to committee, saving us. He looked at me and said, 'You so-and-so,' and I said, 'Rudy, answer me one question. You had more fun today running around talking and all that stuff than you've had in a helluva long time—and admit it.' He looked at me and he smiled and walked away. He was a good friend. His son, Dr. Jerry Schenken, is now one of the leaders in pathology."

While the time and effort required to be an AMA delegate was sometimes tiring and frustrating, Barger says he had a great time with Schenken and with Dr. Bob Brown of Carson City, another AMA delegate. Even today, decades later, Barger still proudly wears Brown's unique gift to him from those days: a Western string tie in the shape of the state of Nevada.

Barger recalls that he also enjoyed the time he spent with Senator Nick Horne; Horne was an executive with the Clark County Medical Society. "Nick Horne was a great guy. Everyone who knew him liked him," Barger observes.

In 1980, when Barger was named senior pathologist, consultant, and quondam chairman at Sunrise Hospital, he was sixty-three years old. Despite the fact that he had attained senior citizen status by then, he was still known as a runner, having maintained his passionate devotion to the sport throughout the decades. Slaughter says he can remember that Barger was still going out jogging at night in his sweats well into his seventies. An avid sports fan, Barger attended nearly every one of the summer Olympic competitions at that time.

The year Barger became senior pathologist at Sunrise, 1980, was a momentous one for him. After living alone as a widower for the previous nine years, he was happily reunited with his old flame, Janie, that special woman in his life whom he had first met as an undergraduate. Janie had been widowed after losing her husband to hepatitis. Barger and Janie were married in 1980, more than four decades after their college courtship.

Barger says he suspects that Janie had married her first husband during World War II against her mother's wishes. He recalls Janie's mother's reaction later, when Janie became Mrs. Barger. "Her mother didn't say so, but she greeted me like, 'Boy, it's about time!'"

Seven years later, in 1987, Barger decided it was time to retire. He looked forward to many years of happiness with Janie, the love of his life.

A Quietly Unassuming Retirement

1987–1999

LAS VEGAS, NEVADA

Today, when Barger looks back on his life, he unhesitatingly states that the thing he is most proud of is having had the opportunity to serve as president of the Nevada Society of Pathologists, from 1967 to 1968. He still attends meetings once in awhile and is on some of the committees, he says. There is still a pathology society but, says Barger, it hasn't met in years. He says that when he was working as a pathologist, "people were more congenial, a thing that I miss now. We just don't have those things anymore."

He became a widower once again in 1991, when his wife, Janie, died. In remembering Janie, Barger emphasizes again that she was really the love of his life. Unfortunately, she was a smoker who was always intending to quit, he says.

"She was always quitting, and she just didn't have any lungs left. After Janie died, typical addict, I'd find packs of cigarettes hidden here and there," Barger says.

"After Janie died, somebody said to me, 'You bury a wife every twenty years,' and I said, 'I don't expect to be around to do it again,'" says Barger.

Age eighty-two as of May, 1999, Barger describes his health as being "all right," and says he has no complaints. He reveals that he does like to light up a cigar every once in awhile.

"I have a pacemaker. And I know that when they turn the pacemaker off, forget it," he says, laughing. "You know the technicians? They love to play with it, run it up and down and everything, and they turn it off and I go, 'Whoops!' I say, 'Wait, wait, wait.' But it works okay now," he says.

He keeps in touch with his children, who are all grown now. Though most of them no longer live in Las Vegas, all remain in the West. His daughter Susan, who has a Ph.D. in material science, lives in Santa Fe, New Mexico. Mary Elizabeth, whom he still calls by her childhood nickname, "Tutubet," also lives in New Mexico, in Albuquerque. "She has an advanced degree in aeronautical and astronomical engineering," Barger states proudly. "She's an expert on the burning of solid fuel rockets."

His youngest son, Michael, graduated from the University of Nevada School of Medicine and now practices rheumatology in Sacramento. Barger's eldest son, Jim, lives in Las Vegas. "He's an expert in computers," says Barger. "He really is."

While Barger has been fully retired since 1987, he says that "The only thing I do is in quality—no, I don't like to use that word—is precision control. It used to be known as quality control." He adds that he has been thinking for awhile about writing something on laboratory precision. Again, he prefers to refer to it as laboratory precision rather than laboratory quality, saying the term "quality" is overused.

"It's really simple to put together in the laboratory. The trouble with most people when they start out in this quality business is they immediately make it complicated—and it isn't," says Barger simply.

These days, Barger can be found engrossed in a book, working a crossword puzzle, or at his computer in his study, quietly enjoying his retirement years in his comfortable, modest home in Las Vegas. He smiles his genial smile often and chuckles, especially when tickled by something he comes across in the mail or when telling a humorous anecdote about his years as a pathologist.

This unassuming fellow in casual slacks, shirt, and a Nevada-shaped string tie especially enjoys showing off family photos to visitors who probably have no inkling of what their host accomplished during his lifetime. They would probably never suspect that this master of understatement worked for decades in the drama of national politics, always playing his part far from center stage. Quietly working in the wings, Dr. James D. Barger made his mark by bringing medical care for the people of Las Vegas into the twentieth century.

Young Jim Barger in Bismarck, North Dakota, circa 1918 (James D. Barger, M.D. photo).

Undergraduate Jim Barger at the University of North Dakota in 1938. (James D. Barger, M.D. photo).

The summer before medical school in 1939, James Daniel Barger cavorts with his future wife, Janie Ray Regan (James D. Barger, M.D. photo).

Las Vegas' Sunrise Hospital as it appeared in the early 1960s, just before Dr. James Barger became director and chairman of the hospital's Department of Pathology (Sunrise Hospital photo).

A bearded Dr. James Barger in the Army of the United States in Riberalta, Bolivia, 1945. (James D. Barger, M.D. photo).

Dr. James Barger and his wife, Janie Regan Barger, in 1981, one year after their marriage (James D. Barger, M.D. photo).

Dr. James Barger enjoying retirement at home in Las Vegas, Nevada, in 1998 (Photo by Annie Blachley).

Clark County Indigent Hospital in 1931. Leonard Kreisler, M.D. suggested
the hospital's current name, University Medical Center of Southern Nevada
(University Medical Center of Southern Nevada photo).

This early 1930s photo
depicts young Len
Kreisler with his par-
ents and sister at
home in White Plains,
New York (Leonard
Kreisler, M.D. photo).

Dr. Leonard Kreisler and his bride, Joan, at their 1957 wedding, just one week before his graduation from medical school (Leonard Kreisler, M.D. photo).

University Medical Center of Southern Nevada, 1976 (University Medical Center of Southern Nevada photo).

Dr. Leonard Kreisler, Captain, U.S. Army Medical Corps, in the late 1950s (Leonard Kreisler, M.D. photo).

(top) Dr. Leonard Kreisler in a graduation photo at the University of Vermont College of Medicine in 1957 (Leonard Kreisler, M.D. photo). *(bottom)* University Medical Center of Southern Nevada Chief of Staff Leonard Kreisler, M.D., in 1982. Dr. Kreisler was instrumental in changing the hospital's name from Southern Nevada Memorial Hospital and in starting the hospital foundation and children's telethon (University Medical Center of Southern Nevada photo).

Participating physician Leonard Kreisler, M.D., at the U.S. Olympic Training Center in Colorado Springs, Colorado, in 1982 (Leonard Kreisler, M.D. photo).

A happily retired Dr. Leonard Kreisler dons his beloved cowboy hat at home in Las Vegas, 1998 (Photo by Annie Blachley).

4

Leonard Kreisler, M.D.

General Practitioner; Medical Director, Department
of Energy Atomic Testing Program (Board Certified by
American Academy of Family Practice and American
Board of Occupational and Environmental Medicine);
Cruise Ship Physician; Years Practiced: 1960–1994

Don't get Vegasized. Do the best job

you can do. Don't get tempted by the

fast buck, the big kill—you know, the

lights, the glamour. Enjoy your

family and take care of the patients.

—Leonard Kreisler, M.D.

The Immigrant Carpenter's Son

1930–1948

BROOKLYN & WHITE PLAINS, NEW YORK

Dr. Leonard Kreisler loves southern Nevada. He loves the climate, the people, the authentic Western flavor—and he's even got the well-worn cowboy hat and boots to prove it. Each year he eagerly awaits the return of the National Finals Rodeo as it gallops into his home town of Las Vegas, and any time of year he flashes a big grin at the mere mention of the event. He's got the state history down cold, too: Ask him about the motto on the Nevada state flag ("battle born"), and he instantly comes up with the little-known fact that back in 1864 while the Civil War was raging, Nevada's statehood was rushed in to get President Abraham Lincoln the votes Lincoln needed for the anti-slavery amendment to the Constitution. There's no doubt about it: this fellow is a Nevadan through and through.

Yet even though he has spent the past twenty-six years of his life in the desert oasis that possesses, arguably, the most relaxed, laid-back lifestyle in the southwest, this physician has never really shed his tough New York skin. While the years have seen him slow down and mellow a bit, Len Kreisler will probably always be as feisty as a neighborhood street kid, the kind of guy who stands up for his beliefs and goes to bat for those causes he supports. A passionate, outspoken advocate of pure health care delivery by Las Vegas' University Medical Center of Southern Nevada (UMC)—Clark County's only publicly owned hospital—Kreisler's legacy includes the hospital's name being changed from Southern Nevada Memorial Hospital to UMC. It was Kreisler who suggested the new name, to more adequately reflect UMC's affiliation with the medical school and to attract patients. Kreisler was also instrumental in starting the UMC Foundation and its involvement with the Children's Miracle Network Telethon.

Still voicing his strong convictions unflinchingly ("gambling is going to ruin the country, the way it's going," he insists), Kreisler has not strayed far from his call-it-like-you-see-it New York upbringing. Never one to mince words, he freely offers a scathing indictment of what happens to some doctors new to Las Vegas.

"I sort of coined a word for myself for the doctors coming into town. Over the years I've noticed they get 'Vegasized.' They get carried away with money and glitz, and the practice of medicine takes a back seat to a jet-set style of life."

Yet Kreisler also has the capacity to lighten up, to not take things so seriously, and share a good laugh. He likes to tell a story about the doctor in the Las Vegas suburb of Henderson who was allegedly exchanging prescriptions for sexual favors in the office. Kreisler's humorous—and topical—take on the doctor's behavior: "He should have run for President!"

Fiercely independent, proud, Kreisler is a true maverick, a nonconformist in the best sense of the word. His deeply abiding sense of ethics has always motivated him to do more than just the minimum, even when that means testing uncharted waters. He originally came to Las Vegas to serve as medical director at the atomic testing program's Nevada Test Site, but quickly went out on a limb to bring a much-needed innovation to the workers there: the old-fashioned concept of family-oriented medical care. He could've stopped at that point, but instead, he involved himself in his adopted community by working on hospital committees, serving as chief of staff of UMC, and throwing his hat in the political arena. For Kreisler, the motivation has always been simple: improve medical care.

Understanding what drives this individual who can be both charming and challenging is easy when one looks at his heritage. He was the first-born son of Harry and Ida Kreisler, immigrant parents who faced adversity head-on, yet turned the experience into a success story. They were two of the many European Jews forced to endure great prejudice before coming to America.

"The early years sound like the often-repeated stories of immigrant parents leaving religious and economic persecution in the early 1900s, coming to this country with nothing but the clothes on their backs and a burning desire to work hard, send their children to college, and live in relative peace," says Kreisler.

Len's father, Harry, had been born into a Jewish family living in Europe during a time of tremendous turmoil over territory, religion, and economics. Just after the beginning of the twentieth century, the Cossack soldiers of Czarist Russia were routinely attacking the homes of Jewish residents, simply because the Jews were of a different race and religion. The practice still survives today all over the world—now it is labeled as ethnic cleansing—but today, as then, it is an inexcusable expression of intolerance. In the early 1900s, Harry Kreisler struggled to survive amid political and economic unrest, as the borders of countries in and around Russia, Poland, and other neighboring countries were constantly redrawn.

"My father came to this country when he was ten or eleven from Austria, from an area which, one day, was Austria, another day was Poland. It was a place called Gilesia, and I don't think it exists anymore. I don't know who owns it now," explains Kreisler. He adds with pride, "He came by himself, with a box of tools. He was a very skilled self-taught cabinetmaker. He became a carpenter and a small-time contractor."

Len Kreisler's mother, Ida Arbeitmen, had also come to America on her own when she was about fourteen or fifteen years old. She came from not too far away in Russia, says Kreisler, in the Ukraine. Like countless others who fled from religious persecution during the great immigrant wave of 1920s America, Ida landed in the great melting pot of cultures, New York City, where she met and married Harry Kreisler. They had two children, a boy and a girl.

"I'm essentially a first-generation American. My sister and I were born here," notes Kreisler. He was born on August 3, 1930. His place of birth and early upbringing—Brooklyn, New York—explain his New York accent, which still comes through loud and clear.

When Len was a two year-old toddler, Harry and Ida Kreisler decided to leave New York City and move the family up to White Plains, New York. As Kreisler puts it, "I was born in Brooklyn, 1930, but luckily my family saw the light and they moved up to White Plains."

The county seat of Westchester County, the White Plains of 1932 was considered very rural, with a population of only 30,000. Kreisler describes the town as very countrified at that time.

"It's about an hour north of New York City. I grew up as a country boy, essentially, with a garden and chickens and the whole bit. Growing up in that area from age two until high school graduation holds many fond rural memories of fishing, gardening, working on cars, and painting the house."

During the years before World War II, Harry Kreisler worked as a cabinetmaker-contractor, and Ida Kreisler stayed home with the children as a housewife, as was the case with most families of the day. Time was taken up much differently then, before television, computers, and other electronic inventions became all-pervasive in the lives of most people. Kreisler counts among the beloved memories of his childhood his memory of playing old-fashioned games such as kick the can and blindman's buff. As a young boy whiling away the hours of those humid Eastern summer months, he loved waiting for the Good Humor man, dapper in white uniform and cap, with the shiny white ice cream truck— especially if young Len got a "Lucky Stick," which meant a free second ice cream.

He recalls being told that he seemed to always want to become a doctor. He says, in fact, that his mother still remembers that as a three year-old, he emphatically told the family doctor that he was going to become a physician so that he could get even and take out the doctor's tonsils. Actually, there was never really any choice in the matter of what Len Kreisler would be when he grew up.

"The family tradition was always: strong work ethic, you got to get an education, you know, that sort of thing," he recalls.

Kreisler went on to excel at his studies, graduating in the top ten percent of a class of more than five hundred students. By then there was no doubt in the mind of that determined seventeen year-old lad from Brooklyn: medicine would be his chosen field.

A Country Boy in the Real World: Prejudice, Premed, and Proving Himself

1948–1953

MEADVILLE, PENNSYLVANIA
BAR HARBOR, MAINE

After graduating from White Plains High School in 1948 Kreisler went to "what was considered by my guidance counselor to be the 'Harvard of the West,'" he says. Allegheny College, in Meadville, Pennsylvania, was just forty miles south of Erie and ninety miles north of Pittsburgh. It was Len's first year away from home, one that took a lot of adjusting for the cabinetmaker's son.

"Not only was the premed academic program demanding, but my social life was somewhat stressful in that I encountered the same bigotry and perceived class distinctions in the fraternities and social clubs, albeit more subtle and polished," notes Kreisler. "It still hurt when apparent close friends said you couldn't join a group because your pedigree or religion was somehow not quite right."

But Len was not deterred by the insidious attitudes that lingered in America in those post-war years: he was, after all, the offspring of tough stock who had battled prejudice all their lives. Kreisler says he inherited more than just the drive to succeed from his parents: they also instilled in him their philosophy of how to evaluate and treat others.

"I feel very fortunate indeed to have gained the insight from them of judging a person by what they think and how they act from the heart—and not by the accumulations they pile up."

Exhibiting the same tenacity and love of education as his parents, Kreisler sought to distinguish himself in many ways as a hard-working premed student. He was a member of Phi Beta Phi, the honorary biology club, and worked as a laboratory assistant in zoology for two years. He also became active in other campus activities, joining the Psychology Club and the German Club ("I was fluent in German," he notes). Scholarships from the American Cancer Society's Crawford County Chapter

127

in Pennsylvania enabled him to spend the summers of 1951 and 1952 at Jackson Laboratories in Bar Harbor, Maine, first as a student and later as a research assistant.

Those were very formative years, working with Dr. George Snell, who would later get a Nobel Prize for tissue transplantation studies, and with other leaders in the fields of basic cancer research. One of the mentors Kreisler looked up to was a Ph.D. immunologist, Dr. Norman Molomut.

"We were doing research that involved host defense mechanisms. Today, it has been taken many steps further, particularly with respect to immunology, monoclonal and tumor-specific antibodies, interferon, et cetera," explains Kreisler.

It was during this time that Kreisler also saw some of his own research findings published in the top-ranked journal *Science* ("The Effect of Heparin on the Growth of a Transplantable Lymphosarcoma in Mice"), in *Proceedings of the National Academy of Sciences* ("Preliminary Report on the Experimental Induction of Metastases from a Heterologous Cancer Graft in Mice"), and in *The American Journal of Pathology* ("Histopathology of Host-Induced Alterations in the Strain Specificity of Sarcoma I in Mice").

After distinguishing himself further by becoming a biology instructor at college, it appeared that some of the fraternities that had snubbed him earlier had a change of heart. Kreisler recalls that they were ready to offer what he calls "a 'limited' social membership."

"It was with a great deal of satisfaction that I told them what they could do with their limited offer." He adds that he also found an ironic sense of satisfaction in the last year of his undergraduate training: elected to Phi Beta Kappa, he went on to earn his bachelors of science in medicine and graduate cum laude.

After graduating from Allegheny College in 1952, Kreisler spent the summer at the Jackson Laboratories in Maine conducting cancer and genetic research. He was able to work as a research fellow after receiving a scholarship from the Westchester, New York chapter of the American Cancer Society.

While Len was in the process of applying to medical school, he encountered another incident of hypocrisy and questionable dealings in the hallowed halls of academia. He recalls that his father called one of the schools and was informed that if he would give a $10,000 donation to Baltimore's prestigious Johns Hopkins University, "they would see what could be done" to get Len admitted.

"Not only was this considered a fortune, but the implication itself infuriated me," states Kreisler. Time proved him correct when he was accepted at five medical schools—strictly on his own merits.

Medical School and Army Research

1953–1960

NEW YORK CITY

BURLINGTON, VERMONT

FORT DETRICK & FORT RITCHIE, MARYLAND

Len Kreisler started medical school at Flower and Fifth Avenue Hospital in New York City with every intention of completing his education there, but several things made him change his mind. Because he was given the opportunity to do further research, he decided to take a year off after completing his first year of medical school. Besides, it didn't take him long to realize he was still a country boy at heart. As he puts it, "I hated New York City."

His research findings on transplanted tumors in mice were again published in *The American Journal of Pathology*, and his manuscript on "Hormone Therapy of the Degenerative Diseases" received honorable mention in the 1953 Schering Essay Contest. After completing a year of research at Waldemar Medical Research in Long Island, New York, Kreisler continued with his second year of medical school, transferring to the University of Vermont school of medicine in Burlington, Vermont. He describes the change of scene from New York City to the picturesque Vermont town with four simple words: "That was like heaven."

Another reason for his delight at attending school in Vermont stems from his attraction to a certain undergraduate female named Joan Dorfman. Kreisler used to kid her about being one the girls who liked to eat at the hospital coffee shop so they could get to meet the medical students—actually, her dormitory was right next to the hospital, and that was the closest place for them to get food, he explains. One week before his graduation from medical school in 1957, Len and his favorite undergraduate were married.

After graduating as an M.D., Dr. Kreisler started his year of rotating internship at Grasslands Hospital in Valhalla, New York, the county hospital of Westchester County (Grasslands Hospital is now part of New

York Medical College). His wife, Joan, taught school in the nearby town of Scarsdale, New York, and the newlyweds lived in a room at the hospital.

In 1958, after completing his internship and passing the national boards, Len went into the army by signing up on the Berry Plan. Kreisler explains that the program gave those who were subject to the draft the chance to volunteer and thereby earn extra money each month (Kreisler calls them "obligated volunteers"). The six weeks of basic training at Fort Sam Houston in San Antonio, Texas, were a real eye-opener, introducing him to cockroaches, flash floods, and huge steaks for only $1.95.

"It was the first time I met a rabbi with a southern drawl and ate ethnic food that bore no resemblance to what New Yorkers claimed as their birthright," Kreisler says.

He had planned to put in for a tour of duty, but when the army found out about his research background he was sent to Fort Detrick, Maryland; there he was assigned to a Walter Reed Army Hospital team doing experiments with anthrax, plague, and other types of bacteriologic warfare agents.

"Fort Detrick is still there," notes Kreisler. "In fact, when the Desert Storm war came up and Saddam Hussein was going to use bacteriologic warfare, Fort Detrick was in the news. They wondered where all the vaccines were—nobody had the vaccines. One of the things that was evident when we were there—I think it's still probably true—is that if you start throwing bacteriologic bombs around, or aerosols, you can't control them. So you may kill your own people just as well. Unless you have specific vaccines or antidotes, you can unleash something that you might regret."

"When we had the scare here (in Nevada), with this guy that supposedly had the vial of plague that he was carrying around, they sent it back to Fort Detrick to be analyzed," Kreisler adds.

After a year at Fort Detrick, Kreisler realized that he would rather work with patients then continue with research. So he asked for a transfer, and was assigned in 1959 to the underground "Pentagon" as a post surgeon at Fort Ritchie, Maryland, about twenty-five miles from Fort Detrick and some sixty miles from Washington, D.C. He describes Fort Ritchie as an idyllic post built during the Depression by the Civilian Conservation Corps, or CCC (the CCC was a program which enlisted unemployed American youths in peacetime army-like units, to aid in reforestation and other public works projects).

"Fort Ritchie was nestled in the Catoctin Mountains about ten miles from Camp David," Kreisler remembers. "It housed about 1,200 military and their dependents, and in case of war, the President and his staff would move underground in that area." The post went on alert every time the President visited neighboring Camp David. Kreisler was just like the family doctor for this post, he says, as well as being the only physician.

Those were memorable times for Kreisler—so memorable that he has promised to someday write a book about what he describes as two really enjoyable years. He maintains, in fact, that had he been guaranteed a residency, he would have re-enlisted and made a career of the military.

One of a Vanishing Breed: Caring for People from Cradle to Grave

1960–1973

HIGHLAND FALLS, NEW YORK
PEEKSKILL, NEW YORK

When Dr. Kreisler mustered out of the service in 1960, he went to join Dr. Abe Margolis, a fellow in general practice in Highland Falls, New York, right at the entrance to West Point. But he found the office to be rather cramped quarters, he says, so he moved back across the Hudson River to Peekskill, New York, about thirty minutes north of his parents' home in White Plains.

"I did full-time family practice for about thirteen years, delivering babies, everything from cradle to grave: putting in stitches, setting bones, making house calls, holding people's hands, and enjoying the privilege of really serving basic needs," recalls Kreisler.

But while his practice was doing well and he enjoyed caring for his patients, the day-in-day-out reality of working eighteen hours a day as a solo general practitioner was beginning to be too much, he says. "I advertised for anybody to come in to the area and cover or become partners. Nobody was interested in general practice, which was unfortunate, because the area had about 100,000 people. I don't think we had more than five or six general practitioners, really, and they were slowly disappearing."

Although Kreisler's practice was huge and successful, a change was imminent. By this time, the Kreisler family had expanded to include two boys, Kevin and Kenneth, and a girl, Kay; Kreisler felt that the children were the right age for a move. In 1969, the family doctor found himself facing the dilemma that frequently confronts many solo practitioners during their careers. Should he break up the home office? Should he continue looking for an associate? Should he move into another type of medical practice in another part of the country? Kreisler started looking around for other things to do.

"I was going to make a career change if I could find the right place—and if I didn't do it then, I wouldn't do it ever," Kreisler remembers. "I wanted, essentially, a warmer climate, different type of work than what I was doing, and definitely, since we were Jewish, we wanted somewhat of a Jewish community."

In 1973, Dr. Kreisler decided to close his old-fashioned home-office general practice. He says that his patients knew, then, that he was probably the last of a vanishing breed.

"No more would they be able to get house calls, twenty-four-hour direct phone contact with a physician, and have someone who took care of them and knew the family from cradle to grave."

But the old-fashioned family practitioner would be well-remembered for years to come. He fondly recalls the time a young woman rang his doorbell, shortly after his move to Las Vegas. "I opened the door and there's a young woman there and she says, 'You don't remember me?' I said, 'No,' and she said, 'You delivered me, back in Peekskill, New York!'"

Kreisler beams at the memory. "That's what I liked about family practice—I mean, that was an old-fashioned home-office combination, and I took care of them."

A Prelude to the Wild, Wild West

1970–1973

LAS VEGAS, NEVADA

Before leaving Peekskill, the Kreislers decided to take a look at Tucson, Arizona, in hopes of settling there. But in 1970, several ads for southern Nevada caught their eye, so they stopped in Las Vegas. It was there the Kreislers began meeting some of the rugged individualists who personified the wild, unbridled West of the early 1970s. One was Dr. Ivan Mindlin, a Las Vegas orthopedist Len and Joan had met earlier during a skiing vacation in Salt Lake City.

"I remembered him in an early publication of *Medical Economics* under the title of 'Doctor on the Strip,'" Kreisler recalls. "Ivan was, and still is, a very, very bright guy, but he had a propensity towards taking chances in gambling, computer stuff and all that. In fact, he at one time was 'the computer doctor' who was brought under indictment."

During the Kreislers visit to Las Vegas, Dr. Mindlin invited them to meet him for dinner late one evening. "By this time it was 10:00 at night. So my wife, Joan, was sitting in the car and he said, 'Come on up, we'll make quick rounds.' While we were making rounds, we bumped into Dr. Friedman, old Dr. Louis Friedman, who was an internist-pulmonologist. This guy comes down the hall in a T-shirt with a porkpie straw hat and a deep Southern accent and he says, 'How ya doin'?' and we got to talking and he says, 'You got to come down and see my office,' and I said, 'You know, it's late. It's 11:00 at night,' and Ivan says, 'You might as well go with him because he's not going to leave you alone,'" recalls Kreisler.

"So we went down to the office and he told me how he was this great internist and pulmonologist and he even was a consultant to the labor unions. He showed me a text that he had written sections for, and showed me some sections on black lung disease that he was a specialist in. He claimed to have known John L. Lewis, from mining lore, when he was head of the United Mine Workers and all that, and then he said if I came to town, he would make me his associate. I said, 'I am not an internist and I am certainly not a pulmonologist'—and he said, it doesn't matter, he'll teach me. I said, 'Thank you very much, but I'll forego that too.'"

A few years later, Dr. Kreisler interviewed with Dr. Jack Cherry. Dr. Cherry had come from Tonopah, Nevada, and was a Las Vegas general practitioner, Kreisler recalls.

"When I saw him and interviewed with him in 1972, he was definitely a character. We were sitting in his office and he said, 'Well, you know, I've got a big practice here and if you come in, you can have it. I'll just turn it over to you. I don't even know what the books are like, you got to talk to my office supervisor to see what the income is. I don't really pay much attention anymore.' He had a cigar that he kept chewing on all the time and puffing every now and then," Kreisler remembers.

"I noticed there was a metal container on his desk, about four inches in diameter, about eight or ten inches long. It had been silvered and it had a screw cap on either end and I said, 'If you don't mind, tell me what's that thing on your desk.' He said, 'Oh, that's interesting. Being a doctor in the early days in Vegas, you'd get a lot of favors and one of the favors was that some of my contacts gave me a jewelry shop at the old Stardust. Of course, you make a lot of cash with something like that. I didn't know what to do with the cash, so I buried it in three cylinders like that. They told me, 'Put it in the ground but make sure it's airtight, watertight, and all that. So I got these metal cylinders with screw caps at either end. I buried them in the ground. When I wanted the cash I went out there and dug them up. Two of them I found relatively easy; THAT son of a gun took me a long time before I found it. When I did find it I took the money out, of course, and I had it silvered as a memento.'"

Kreisler recalls Dr. Cherry telling him it would be no problem at all to get Kreisler full surgical privileges and any other privileges he wanted at Southern Nevada Memorial Hospital (now University Medical Center of Southern Nevada). Kreisler told Dr. Cherry, "Well, I don't do major surgery."

Dr. Cherry answered, "That's no problem at all—we'll get you the privileges."

"I'm thinking then, 'This is really frontier medicine out here,'" recalls Kreisler. "Dr. Cherry was an old institution. When I went though his office it was interesting. He had two televisions up high on pedestals at the end of his office. He had a whole slew of seats that were lined up like a theater facing the television sets, and in his so-called 'treatment room' he had three main medications. He had one closet full of B12 injections, another closet full of various types of hydrocortisone injections, and another closet full of an ointment called ergophene, which was like an icthyal tar ointment with zinc in it. I think Upjohn made it and then discontinued it; he bought it all up.

"So if you came in and complained of anything that was not contagious, infectious, or acute or anything like that, you would probably get a B12 shot to perk you up. If it had anything itching or an allergic connotation to it, he'd give you a shot of cortisone. If you had a skin rash of any kind, you got ergophene," Kreisler explains, adding, "Las Vegas was, apparently, still the old West in some ways."

A Healer for the Nuclear Age

1973–1991

MERCURY & LAS VEGAS, NEVADA

While the Kreislers were looking around Las Vegas, Dr. Kreisler got an offer from Reynolds Electrical and Engineering Company (REECO) to be the medical director for the atomic test program at the Nevada Test Site. With the Cold War that had begun at the end of World War II in 1945 still up and running, nuclear weapons were still being developed. The position REECO offered Kreisler was to start in August, 1973, at what he describes as "a ridiculously low salary." But adapting to change and challenges—not hungering for money—had always come easily to this doctor. Because Reynolds was the prime contractor to the U.S. Department of Energy's Nevada Operations Office, taking the position would mean Kreisler would have to abandon general practice and take up something completely new: occupational medicine.

"But we figured, what the heck, we'd take a chance on it. My wife was for the move and the kids were the right age: Kevin, the oldest, was thirteen, Kay was eleven, and Ken was nine years old," explains Kreisler.

He tells the story of a humorous exchange between another physician and himself which captures the popular conceptions most people had of Las Vegas, and also illustrates his love of playing on those misconceptions. Just before leaving Peekskill, the Kreislers were at a doctor's clambake, when an ear, nose, and throat man asked him why he was leaving and giving up his practice. Kreisler responded, straight-faced, "Well, Harry, if you promise not to tell anybody, I'll tell you the real reason."

"Oh, of course," Harry answered.

"No, Harry, you have to swear," Kreisler insisted.

"I swear."

"Harry, I'm going out to Vegas to be a doctor for the mob. The rest of it is just a façade," Kreisler declared.

"I knew it! I knew it!"

"To this day," Kreisler says, "Harry still believes that. Interestingly enough, I heard that Harry was under indictment for income tax problems back in Peekskill, New York. I don't think he's practicing anymore."

Kreisler's first day on the new job gave the former New Yorker an eye-opening introduction to the southern Nevada desert, and to what he remembers as "really the wild West." Having come straight from New York, he had never really been out in the desert to speak of, Kreisler recalls.

"My first day out, a Dr. Savino W. Cavender ("Beanie" Cavender), a retired military doctor who had been at the Test Site for quite a while and was acting director, asked me if I would go from Mercury up to Area 12, which was another thirty or forty miles from Mercury. It was a total of about 110 miles from Las Vegas. Would I go up and pronounce a guy dead? They found a man in a trailer up there who was dead. So I got in the ambulance and I'm riding up with the paramedic through wasteland. I mean, there's nothing but Yucca, Joshua, and dirt: nothing. And I'm wondering, 'What the heck did I get into?'"

They drove up to a trailer in a little mining camp in Area 12 to find a man sitting at a table in rigor mortis, in a rather grotesque type of pose, as Kreisler tells it. "He had a lot of old froth around his mouth and he looked like he died of acute pulmonary edema. At that time, this guy that I would eventually become very good friends with, Bill Flangas, a mining engineer, comes in and introduces himself as head of maintenance and operations. He said, 'What do you think, doc?' I said, 'Well, it looks like he probably had a heart attack and got a lot of fluid in his lungs that backed up, and I don't see anything suspicious.' He said, 'Yeah, it happens to these old guys.'"

At that point a man who said he was the coroner from Tonopah came into the trailer. Kreisler told him he thought the cause of death was an acute MI (myocardial infarction [heart attack], the death of a segment of heart muscle following interruption of its blood supply) with pulmonary edema (filling up of the lungs with fluid), and that it didn't look like anything suspicious.

"So he said, 'Well, how do you spell that acute what? Pulmonary edema?' I said, 'Well, aren't you a doctor?' He said, 'Hell, no! I'm a gas station owner up in Tonopah. We don't have any doctor coroners. Sometimes we don't even have a doctor in Tonopah.' So I said, 'Oh, okay.' Then I'm really wondering what's going on. This is Nye County, next to Clark County. So I spelled it for him and all that. I said, 'Well, I think we ought to get an autopsy just, you know, for the record. It was an unattended death and all.' He said, 'We don't have money to do autopsies up here. If you want an autopsy, send the body down to Clark County and you have to get the Department of Energy to put up the $200—which we did. That was my introduction to part of my new job and Nye County," says Kreisler.

But Kreisler took to Las Vegas right away. "I loved Las Vegas when we first moved here. I love the heat. I love the sun. It was hot, but to me it was great. I really liked it and, of course, it was a total change in my lifestyle, because here I put in regular hours from, you know, nine or whenever when I reported to work and came home by five or six, and even though I was technically on call, I very rarely got called," he remembers.

As for the patients, he found little difference from those he had treated back East ("I saw the same thing that you did all over"). The one exception, according to Kreisler, was that Clark County was—and still is—among the highest per capita in the nation for lung cancer. "It has nothing to with the environment—we just have a lot of smokers and drinkers," declares Kreisler. "You can't blame that on the Test Site, or construction, or whatever—it's smoking and drinking."

He tells an anecdote about a patient who was smoking in his office, despite the no smoking signs. The patient had had one lung taken out for carcinoma (cancer) of the lung, Kreisler explains. "So I said, 'You're not only smoking in my office when you're not supposed to, but you had a lung removed. Why are you smoking?' He said, "What are you going to do, doc? Take out the other lung?' I mean, he didn't care."

When Kreisler first came to Nevada, he had the perception, like many others, that the quality of medical education and care was better in the East than in the West. "I thought, Harvard, Johns Hopkins, those were the Meccas. But we've got Stanford on the West Coast, which is as good as any other school; we've got the University of California, San Diego, which does good work; great centers in Arizona, great centers in Salt Lake City, Rochester, Minnesota—when you get out here you realize there are centers all over. Great centers have their shortcomings too, just like they do in the East. There's no difference," Kreisler asserts. He adds that people move to Las Vegas from Los Angeles, from New York, and Chicago and say the doctors there are much more qualified. "I say, 'No, they're not. We have very good doctors and we have lousy doctors, just like anyplace else in the country.' The big problem is the patient doesn't know who is who, and doesn't have the time or ability to find out."

"The patient, a lot of times, is to blame, too. They'll go to a good family doctor but right away they'll say, 'I want to see a specialist, because I was brought up in Long Island or wherever, and you've got to see a specialist.'"

For Kreisler, working as the Test Site medical director was radically different from solo family practice. Kreisler says he had "five doctors under me, about eight nurses, forty-something paramedics, ten ambulances, and about a two- to three-million-dollar-a-year budget." He could take care of things over the phone, since he had all this medical staff under him, he explains.

"I thought I'd died and gone to heaven," Kreisler recalls of those early years. "I was making a lot less money, but who cared? The lifestyle was really nice and the town was a lot of fun. There were only 250,000 people—now it's 1,300,000, so it's more than quadrupled. Everybody knew everybody and it was really very, very nice. We had the services that big cities had to offer—yet it was still a relatively small town."

Kreisler says their oldest son, Kevin, who was thirteen at the time, missed his friends a little bit when they first moved to Las Vegas, but it didn't take him too long to adjust. "They (Kreisler's children) loved growing up here. In retrospect, they all say that it was the best move."

Kreisler's office in town was located at the old Rancho Medical, at the corner of Rancho and Sahara. He took care of the people in town, about 3,000 employees, and the rest were out at the Test Site, he says; the site was located sixty-five miles northwest of Las Vegas and four hundred miles southeast of Reno. There were about 8,000 employees in an area the size of Rhode Island, about 14,000 square miles, including all the activities in Las Vegas up to the Tonopah Test Range as well as some special Air Force areas. In the beginning, until Kreisler got things organized the way he wanted, he would go out almost every day, he recalls; then he would go out maybe once or twice a week. Once or twice a month, he'd fly up to the Tonopah Test Range, where a lot of civilians worked.

When Kreisler first arrived, the program was really in the doldrums, as he puts it. He notes that several years before, a doctor who worked for Union Carbide named Dr. Lloyd B. Tepper had been commissioned to do an evaluation of the Test Site medical program.

"A doctor named Ruben Zucker, who was an internist in town, was on that panel, a very fine internist at UMC (University Medical Center)," notes Kreisler. "Ruben was actually instrumental in bringing Dr. Quagliana here, the first oncologist. He was instrumental in setting up an internal medicine residency with a strong liaison with Tulane, and Dr. Birch from Tulane. So that's why we have a lot of doctors in their forties and fifties who had done residencies at Tulane and then come here. Dr. Neal Carmena, an internist who is still practicing in Las Vegas, came from Tulane; he was a little younger than Ruben Zucker. Then we had Enrique Lacayo. Dr. Pablo Joya is another one who is an internist still practicing in town. Quite a few of them came and a lot of them were gastroenterologists. For some reason or other that was big at Tulane."

Kreisler says that Dr. Tepper's evaluation, commissioned in 1970, found an apparent lack of involvement with the local medical community. So when Kreisler took over, he was interested in really looking into the local community to see how he could fit in. He says the panel also made another recommendation: previously, patients had usually been sent into town to an occupational or non-occupational specialist. The panel wanted more practice of medicine at the Test Site.

Kreisler was extremely pleased that he could transfer the concept of old-fashioned family-oriented care to the workers. "I brought the idea of family medicine in there. I was going to treat it as a family," he explains. And that he did: the effect he had on the health of the workers would be illustrated years later by what the wife of one of his former patients told him.

"You're the one who saved my husband's life," she told Kreisler. "He had bad lung disease and you told him he shouldn't be working. In addition to that, you got him Social Security retirement and then he went on to Stanford and got a lung transplant, and he's still living and doing fairly well. If it hadn't have been for you, he probably would have died on the job out in the desert."

Kreisler recalls that despite the panel's recommendations, the Department of Energy said they were a little apprehensive. "They didn't want to get any criticism that I was infringing on the income of local doctors. I told them not to worry, because if anything, if I practiced more, there'd be more referrals and so the local doctors would actually get much more to do—which is what happened. I don't think we ever had any complaints about me treating patients out at the Test Site or those in town."

Because Kreisler still wanted to be in contact with what was going on in the local community, he wrote to all the hospitals to tell them he would be medical director at the Test Site. "I wouldn't be taking care of patients in the hospital, but obviously, with a work force of that size and their dependents, I would probably be referring patients in for care to various hospitals or doctors," he recalls.

"The only hospital that ever answered was Southern Nevada Memorial Hospital, now UMC (University Medical Center of Southern Nevada). Radiologist Dr. Harry Knudson was chief of staff. He sent me a very warm letter saying that I'd be welcome to come to the hospital anytime, join the staff, and be as active as I wanted to."

The hospital situation in Las Vegas was totally foreign as compared to what went on back East, notes Kreisler. In Peekskill, there had been just one hospital, a community hospital; but in Las Vegas there was one teaching/not-for-profit hospital and another not-for-profit hospital, Rose De Lima (now known as Saint Rose Dominican Hospital). Kreisler observes that the other hospitals "were definitely FOR PROFIT in big capital letters, and they obviously weren't interested in me, because I didn't admit patients. I guess they didn't realize that I would be influencing the referral of at least two or three hundred patients into some type of hospital care over each year—and as time went on, it got to be probably more."

Kreisler became as knowledgeable as he could about what was going on in town, joining Clark County Medical Society and becoming a member of its executive committee as well as many other committees. He established a blood donor program for the Test Site and served on the Community Blood Services advisory board. A member of the American College of Emergency Physicians, Kreisler was elected a Fellow of the American Occupational Medical Association in 1978. He served as counselor-delegate to the Nevada State Medical Association and was nominated as a delegate for 1979 and 1980, and lent his expertise to many advisory boards and programs, notably in the areas of drug abuse, rehabilitation, and occupational medicine. His articles continued to be printed in such publications as *Applied Radiology* and *Journal of Medicine,* and he served as editor and producer of *Department of Energy/ DOCS,* a newsletter for Department of Energy physicians and contractor physicians. In 1982, his love of sports won him an invitation to be a participating physician at the U.S. Olympic training center at Colorado Springs, Colorado, and he was appointed a University of Nevada School of Medicine preceptor; in 1983 he was appointed clinical assistant professor in the department of family and community medicine. He also established an optional occupational medicine rotation for medical students and residents at the medical school.

Kreisler says he was very happy as an active staff member of Southern Nevada Memorial (SNMH), where he held office and served on several committees. Elected chief of staff of the hospital from 1982 to 1983,

Kreisler says he brought up the fact that the hospital's name should be changed to University Medical Center of Southern Nevada (UMC), to reflect the nature of the teaching center and its affiliation with the University of Nevada School of Medicine; the hospital is the major Southern Nevada clinical campus of the medical school.

"It would also be a much better marketing tool: newcomers would prefer to go to a 'university-affiliated' hospital. We pushed the name change through with the help of hospital administrator George Riesz and Joe Denny, another hospital official. I was surprised that we didn't get more opposition from the private hospitals. I think it has been of value to the community and to the hospital that we did change the name at that time," says Kreisler. The name change became official in 1986.

While he was chief of staff, Kreisler also asked Riesz why the hospital didn't have a foundation. Kreisler wondered, "The hospital's been here for fifty years and it's the only hospital of its kind in southern Nevada—and no one except Claude Howard had ever really given any money of significance. Riesz explained to me 'the realities of life:' any time a foundation for SNMH was discussed, the private hospitals would kill it. So that was a challenge. The private hospitals did not—and still do not—welcome any competition from this hospital."

So Kreisler began making waves, speaking up and spearheading the drive to organize a foundation for the hospital that was the only not-for-profit teaching hospital in Las Vegas. The UMC Foundation would consist of a group of dedicated Las Vegas residents interested in informing the public as to what the hospital was all about, and helping to raise money for much-needed projects. Their goal: raise one million dollars to assist the hospital, particularly the children's ward. In 1982 Kreisler went to Bill Flangas, the mining engineer he had first met when pronouncing the man dead at the trailer in Nye County. By this time Kreisler and Flangas had become friends; Flangas was a native Nevadan from Ely and head of maintenance and operations at the Test Site, explains Kreisler. The two invited forty-five people to a hospital luncheon, including Ann Valder, who wrote for the *Las Vegas Review-Journal* and the *Las Vegas Sun*, he recalls, and was very supportive of the hospital.

"She was there and she suggested other key people for the luncheon. Out of that group we got seven or eight people to actually commit," remembers Kreisler. "For the privilege of starting this foundation, we each chipped in $200, because we didn't have any money. We had no support from the county commissioners, which has been true up to this day, even though the commissioners sit as the board of directors."

But they had the support of former governor Grant Sawyer ("very, very strong in the Democratic party," as Kreisler observes). They wrote up a charter and got the group together: founding members Bill Flangas; Carolyn Sparks, who would later become a regent at University of Nevada, Las Vegas, or UNLV ("from an old-time Las Vegas family," says Kreisler), Stan Colton, also from an old-time family; Earl Johnson, who ran the *Las Vegas Review-Journal*; and Sylvia Maxson, whose husband, Robert C. Maxson, was president of UNLV. Adds Kreisler, "We also got Bill Morris, who was a great guy. He wasn't a native Nevadan, but he went to school here and one of his claims to fame was that he was a member of the 1947 or '48 Vegas High football team that had never been defeated. They called him Wildcat Morris; a very, very nice guy. The story goes that he put about $20,000 into the old Holiday Inn on the Strip and cashed out twenty years later with many millions. He put it into the old Landmark Hotel, and that was his swan song. Tom Raines was a very dedicated guy to the hospital. He runs the annual softball game for the children's telethon and then he is still a member of the board; Angie Wallin, who had a lot of local clout; Carl Apple, who was an accountant; and some other people."

Kreisler reveals that the original founding members were pressured by the private hospitals, as illustrated by Grant Sawyer's announcement to Kreisler following a foundation meeting. After working with the group for several years, Sawyer told Kreisler he was resigning because of pressure from Sunrise Hospital, which Sawyer represented.

"I said I understood and I appreciated the fact that he was in there in the first two years, which were, you know, the toughest years for the foundation. Riding down in the elevator I remember him saying very clearly, 'You know, the commissioners don't really want this foundation to be around, and certainly the private hospitals don't, either.' Personally, he was very supportive and we appreciated that. He passed away, I think, a year or two ago."

What really got the foundation cemented, recalls Kreisler, was that in its first year local radiologist Dr. Steve Kollins was doing business with Gary Sheets of Salt Lake City, who mentioned a children's telethon there. The annual Osmond's Children Telethon was one year old, and its charter specified that only teaching hospitals—either solely pediatric hospitals, children's hospitals, or those with a major pediatric service—could participate. The telethon was set up so that all funds raised in each locale would remain in that area for children's medical care.

"The only hospital that qualified in southern Nevada, was, of course,

UMC," explains Kreisler. He recalls that they got in touch with the Osmond people and one of their two leaders who were running the telethon came down. But he told Kreisler he doubted whether they could really get into it at that time, because the foundation had just been formed.

"We said, 'No, we're going to go ahead and do it anyway,'" says Kreisler. "So we jumped in. We went to Jim Rogers of Channel Three. For the big sum of, I think it was either $4,300 or $4,500, he agreed to block out the twenty hours and give us the studio and the time and then after the telethon, he donated it back to us. So the first year, it cost us essentially nothing. This was a magnificent gift that Jim Rogers gave to medical care in southern Nevada—one of many gifts he has given."

Kreisler remembers that they went after all the doctors for contributions and raised $20,000. "In fact, Dr. Elias Ghanem gave $1,000—I don't know if he realizes to this day what it was all about! Carl Apple, his accountant, set up the meeting with Elias, who had nothing to do with UMC, and we told him we were going to have a children's telethon. I guess he figured he'd be on television or something, so he gave us the money. This really was humorous to us, but we thanked him for the gift, as well as a few other doctors who really didn't like UMC but who didn't understand what was going on: we came on so fast! We raised another ten during the telethon and we were off and running, raising a total of $30,000 that first year. We had essentially no expenses. Everything was donated."

Betty Gilday ran the telethon, remembers Kreisler. "She was formerly married to a movie star, so she was familiar with TV productions and all. She scripted the telethon and ran the whole thing. We were very successful. We raised equal to or more money than many of the other participants in that second year of the Children's Miracle Network Telethon."

As Kreisler describes it, from then on it was history. By 1991, the year the local telethon raised $452,000, the foundation's goal of one million dollars in donations and contributions to the hospital had been more than realized. Kreisler says the publicity and everything that went along with that was so great that the private hospitals couldn't stop the foundation anymore. "That really got it going—we were well-entrenched. From 1982 to 1998, I think it has raised well over three or four million dollars in cash, which stays in the community. The annual publicity that goes along with the telethon is priceless."

Kreisler says it is interesting to note that other hospitals followed UMC Foundation's lead. He says that every year just before the telethon, Sunrise Hospital created what they called "their children's hospital, which it's not. It's just a floor. They would come on with very heavy advertising to promote their children's services. Recently Valley Hospital even put on a children's E.R.—so not only has UMC been the cutting edge for all of these children's services, taking on burn care, emergency services, intensive care services for children and all, but we've stimulated these other hospitals to go ahead and extend their services. They're doing it, in my opinion, for the wrong reasons, but at least they're doing it. So we positively, very strongly, affected our health delivery care in southern Nevada with the foundation. It's now raising at least a half a million a year."

With the telethon firmly established, Kreisler decided in 1986 that the time was right for him to try to bring about another type of hospital improvement. At the time, he had the naïve belief that as a doctor he could point out to the public that the UMC hospital board was composed of the county commissioners, who had very little interest in the hospital.

"I thought if I ran for the county commission in District E it would be a positive thing. Unfortunately, I had switched parties and was running as a Republican, which was not big in that district. A lot of other things came into play, like the fact that Hank Greenspun (publisher of the *Las Vegas Sun*) didn't like me very much, and so a week before the election he came out with a big article with a bunch of negative adjectives which, of course, had no basis in fact."

Kreisler called Mike O'Callaghan, whom he knew personally, and asked, "Is this responsible reporting?" "Well, you know, they did that to me when I was governor. That's politics," was O'Callaghan's response. While that was not responsible reporting, said O'Callaghan, what could Kreisler do about it? "Are you going to spend $1,800 for a full-page ad that's going to get you nowhere? Just realize that you are probably overqualified for the job anyway," O'Callaghan told Kreisler. Kreisler's reply: "Mike, thanks. That's a compliment."

Four years later, in 1990, Kreisler ran again. "Luckily, I lost in the primary by two hundred votes because the lawyer who ran against me and who happens to be a big medical malpractice lawyer against doctors in town, Gary Logan, spent big money and got very little more than I got in the previous election," Kreisler recalls.

"To run for county commission, you needed $100,000 or more, minimum: that was in '86. By 1990 you had to be ready to spend $300,000 or more because that's what they were spending. If it's a real contested election, like the one where Christensen was ousted by Lance Malone, you're talking $500,000. He got $200,000 from Sheldon Adelson alone because Adelson wanted Christensen out in a bad way," Kreisler notes.

"Incidentally, Christensen was never a friend of UMC. He hated the hospital. There are tapes somewhere, where TV reporters recorded a big blow-up between Christensen and myself. He just didn't want to help the hospital, even though he was sitting as a de facto board member. Then when he got prostate cancer, I think he was mellowed in his later years; he wasn't quite as vocal about the hospital—at least that was my impression."

Although he lost the election, Kreisler says he is still looking forward to somebody putting the arm on the commissioners, since they sit as the board of directors, to really get them involved with the UMC Foundation and the hospital.

"To this point, they haven't. It is very political, but that's the way it is," Kreisler asserts. He adds that he finds it a little disturbing that the medical school and the hospital are losing a lot of opportunities to work together. "The dean, Dr. Robert Daugherty, has a legitimate gripe. I spoke to him several years ago. There was nobody at the hospital to communicate with, and he was right—there really isn't anybody that has any vision or interest in promoting health care delivery, pure health care delivery. Everything is involved with politics, competition, conflicting motives, and all that sort of stuff. On the other hand, the dean is going off and developing his own programs. Some of these are going to hurt UMC—there's no question about it. Maybe someday they'll get together seriously and it'll be run by an objective board rather than a political entity. I think that would be very helpful.

"I think the medical school has one agenda, and UMC has another. They're losing a lot of resources. If you combined the financial resources and manpower you could deliver much better health care. It was the same thing in 1986," Kreisler explains. "I told Senator Harry Reid, and I told Senator Chic Hecht, instead of building a combined veterans' and active duty hospital out in Nellis, build a dedicated wing onto UMC: it's cheaper, it's quicker, and it can be staffed by both the hospital and the medical school—it's all there. But they didn't. It's a mess out there as far as the veterans are concerned. They don't have the staffing, and consequently can't cover it adequately."

One problem Kreisler says he has seen over the years is the explosion of doctors coming into Las Vegas. He cites the example of Dr. Tony Marlon, who came to town around 1973, as did Kreisler. "It was Tony Marlon, Ed Quinn and Joe Kaufman, all excellent cardiologists, who set up the first cardiology group at UMC. It was the best in the West! They brought in a Ph.D. exercise physiologist, Dr. Gary Adams, who ran an excellent cardiac rehabilitation program. This was the first group that came in with stress testing, angiography and the rest," Kreisler recalls.

"Then Tony had a bent for being an entrepreneur, so he started Southwest Medical Associates, which then went into the HMO business. Eventually, Ed Quinn went his own way with another cardiology group and Joe left too. Tony went on to become the biggest and only native-grown HMO. In fact, one of the biggest turnouts the county medical society ever had was when Tony Marlon debated Ernie Libman on the virtues of private entrepreneurial medicine versus HMOs. That was one hell of a turnout, sometime in the early to mid-eighties. Ernie Libman, of course, was trained along with David Brandsness (administrator at Sunrise) under Nate Adelson at Sunrise Hospital. Ernie was administrator for Valley Hospital and now North Las Vegas Hospital."

Kreisler notes that UMC has always been criticized by the County Commission for having to come up with $15,000,000 plus or minus every year to bail it out of its shortfall. A longtime defender of UMC, Kreisler says that Tony Marlon told him that an independent survey done in 1987 pinpointed the reason for the shortfall.

"If the county commissioners paid the hospital what was owed for indigent care and/or Medicaid, and the state paid its part, the hospital never would have been in the red. It just wouldn't be. As it was, let's say in 1987, out of a budget of roundly $180,000,000, even if the county had to come up with $10,000,000 or $15,000,000 to break even, that's nothing. That's unheard of in the country, where a county hospital only needs public assistance of $10,000,000 or 15,000,000. Most county hospitals require fifty to one hundred million per year in subsidies."

Kreisler insists that "the hospital has always, despite all the adverse publicity, all the adverse pressure, done a remarkable job. It has been the leader in oncology, in physical medicine and rehabilitation, in pediatric care and, of course, they've got the trauma center, even though Sunrise Hospital was battling for it. That's where it had to be, because that's where they had the full-time residency programs, and so it has come a long way. I just hope it continues that way."

As a longtime Las Vegas physician, Kreisler saw a trend he found disturbing over the years. He says years ago the late Nate Adelson, administrator of Sunrise Hospital, was the original promoter of the idea of giving doctors perks, or "free office space, even cars, as long as they would put their patents in that hospital. I don't know how much of it is done today, but that was accepted practice in those days, and all the private hospitals did it at the time."

He also has a pointed comment to make on the effect Las Vegas has on some doctors who come to town. He says they get "Vegasized."

"As an example, I don't want to mention any names, but there was a young surgeon who came into town; a family man, very well trained, two kids—and the next thing I hear he's going for a divorce, marrying somebody else and accumulating wealth."

But during his early years in Las Vegas, Kreisler was able to remain focused on bringing his own old-fashioned general practice to the people at the Test Site. He was also immersing himself in a whole new field. Like most doctors—with the exception of radiologists—he hadn't had any in-depth exposure to nuclear medicine before taking over as medical director. So he took some courses specifically given by the Department of Energy to familiarize their doctors with radiation medicine; there were approximately thirty medical directors across the country from the various Department of Energy installations, he recalls.

"We took these courses in radiation terminology: what radiation exposure can do, what you would do in case of a nuclear incident, the distinction between contamination or exposure, etc."

After his mini-residency at the University of Cincinnati, plus the other requirements, he sat for his Boards in occupational medicine. By 1980, he had dual boards in family practice and occupational medicine. Until 1990, he was the only board certified occupational medicine doctor in Nevada, he says, adding that there were only about 1,200 in the country at the time.

"It's an interesting Board," says Kreisler. "Most people don't understand that it's shared with the aerospace and public health Boards. The first day of the boards was public health and then the second day, you would take your sub-specialty, which was either public health, aerospace, or occupational, and if you passed both parts, you would get certified in either one of those disciplines."

As to what actually took place at the site during an atomic test, Kreisler says there wasn't really much to see. "Since 1962, all testing out there was below ground, so the old visions of mushroom clouds going up in the air were gone. They drilled a hole up to eighteen feet in diameter and as much as a half a mile deep, as straight as an arrow. They would put the atomic device in a cylinder down this hole, and then line up all the experiments above it in the cylinder. Then all this stuff would be hooked to cables which would come up out of the ground to the recording trailers. Then they would put what they called stemming on the top of the hole, so that when the atomic device blew, it would not come up through the ground. It would cause a molten cavity of material deep below ground which would then cool and harden, so that all the nuclear or radioactive material was essentially encased in a glass-like material down below. That was one type of test."

When the device was ready to go off, the above-ground cameras showed the earth shaking and a little dust going up, as people watched from the control room, says Kreisler. "Then you could see the geophones record the ground motion: that would be an indication of how the cavity was collapsing, and what was going on down below."

As to radiation exposure at the site, Kreisler notes that before he joined the program, there was one incident. He says that in 1970, they had a little of what they call "'venting;' a few noble gasses and vapors escaped from the ground. They got quite concerned. There were several lawsuits subsequently filed by people who said they had exposures to radiation which caused various diseases—but in looking at those claims, I have never seen any that were valid. They just didn't have enough radiation exposure."

Dr. Maxwell Kaye, an internist who worked for the Environmental Protection Agency in Las Vegas, screened claims to see if they had any validity, Kreisler says. "As far as I know, they never paid on any, and they still haven't to this day, for any of the radiation claims from testing at the Nevada Test Site," notes Kreisler.

There were no more than two or three claims a year, Kreisler recalls, when he first took over in 1973. But by the mid-eighties, attitudes about litigation over virtually everything had changed, so that it became the fashion to sue at the slightest inclination, observes Kreisler. "We were getting 1,200 to 1,500 suits a year of 'alleged radiation exposure.' Most of those, including the people in St. George, Utah, really had, in my opinion, no medical basis at all. St. George was downwind from some of the atmospheric tests (not below-ground). Some people from that area have claimed cancers due to above-ground testing.

"Now there were two people, very interestingly, that died at an Air Force Site which is not supposed to exist (Area 51)," Kreisler notes. He says he doesn't know how much he can talk about this without getting into trouble, but does comment on the supposedly nonexistent Area 51.

"I think it's so stupid, because civilian people have climbed the surrounding mountains with telephoto lenses and they've taken photos of the runway, and pictures have been in the *Las Vegas Review-Journal* showing everything out there. The Air Force doesn't want to talk about it. They do whatever the Air Force wants to do for testing. Now, I think the Air Force is stupid the way they handle their public relations and I also think the DOE is stupid with their public relations—but, you know, you're not going to change it: it's a bureaucratic mish-mosh. I mean, it's there, everybody knows it's there, so why not say it's there?"

He explains that two people died there and the allegations were that they died from toxic fumes as a result of PCBs (polychlorinated biphenyls, or toxic materials) being burned for disposal.

"Dr. Thorne Butler was very helpful at the time," recalls Kreisler. "He was one of the few pathologists in the country who was recognized as an expert in toxicology, drug testing and forensic pathology. This guy was a giant and he actually made a deposition on tape for one of these people. Luckily it was on tape, because he subsequently died from a cardiac arrhythmia as I understand, but we had the tape. The people lost the case. I happened to know that one of them died from alcoholic problems, and the other one died from excessive smoking: he died a respiratory death. It had nothing to do with anything else out there. Yet they keep beating it to death that these guys died of toxic this and toxic that, and it's not true. A current Nevada Supreme Court justice, Bill Maupin, was the lead lawyer for our side."

"Television's *60 Minutes* carried this story. When I wrote to them to correct their inaccurate reporting, they never responded," he says.

While at the Test Site, Kreisler set up many innovative programs. One was established with Associated Pathologists Laboratories' Dr. Butler, whom Kreisler describes as a recognized world leader in toxicologic and laboratory pathology. They set up a drug screening program for employees of the Department of Energy and the civilian work force in the mid-1980s. They were one of the first to have such a screening program, notes Kreisler.

"It was interesting that the government workers eventually were exempt from being tested, at least in those early days; we only tested the civilian work force."

Another of Kreisler's innovations was to set up a health track system which put the information on deaths and morbidity (the rate of disease or proportion of diseased persons in a given locality) of workers each year into a computer model, categorized them, and compared the distribution to the deaths in Clark County. They found that they followed the same distribution, says Kreisler.

"The major deaths were from either cancer or cardiovascular problems, and the major reasons for being out of work were the same thing as in any other occupational analysis: respiratory, gastrointestinal, that type of thing." The conclusion reaffirmed Kreisler's oft-stated conviction: "The Test Site was probably one of the safest places to work in the entire United States."

While Kreisler was the site's medical director, there was only one radiation incident, he notes. It involved a person from radiation safety who was demonstrating how to safely handle a radioactive source. "For some unknown reason, he opened up this lead container and actually stuck his hand in and picked the radioactive source up with his bare hand. When he realized what he was doing, he just dropped it back in the shielded container and covered it. They calculated the dose to his hand and forearm as being quite significant." Though the man was monitored for six months, Kreisler says nothing ever happened to him.

"He didn't even get any redness or local changes to his hand or forearm, and he certainly got no systemic (involving the entire body) reaction. Fortunately, there is a very wide margin of safety with respect to radiation exposures."

Kreisler was so confident about the safety of atomic energy and its related benefits that he would give lectures to anyone who was interested, incorporating his sizeable collection of radiation injury slides. He says such slides are hard to come by, because there haven't been that many radiation injuries. Kreisler maintains that even after looking over the data from the Three Mile Island accident, he found nothing indicating any significant radiation exposure.

"It was all contained within the complex, the way it had been designed; the only reactor in this country, a graphite one without all that protection, was an experimental reactor in Hanford, Washington. Now the Russians were building graphite reactors without the containment contingency that we developed, even though they were warned that these were very dangerous. Of course, they had a big problem at Chernobyl. The French, on the other hand, have gone ahead and developed nuclear power to the extent that close to ninety-five percent of their power is nuclear generated. They even sell the power to Germany, probably Spain, and a couple of other countries. Japan is approximately sixty-five percent nuclear powered at this time."

"Our country is twenty percent nuclear powered. It hasn't built a nuclear reactor in fifteen or more years. We have approximately 109 or so nuclear reactors; actually Chicago is fifty percent nuclear powered, which most people don't realize."

As for media accounts of radiation sickness and scenarios of accidental radiation exposure, Kreisler maintains that these are politically driven and scientifically incorrect about ninety-five percent of the time. He insists there were no significant radiation exposures at the Test Site from 1973 to the present, adding that "I had the data to back it up, along with health track material to show that deaths and morbidity of workers at the site were no different than the rest of Nevada."

Kreisler also has strong opinions on comments made by Energy Secretary Bill Richardson in announcing a compensation plan for workers who allegedly became sick while making nuclear weapons. In a story reported by Associated Press in July, 1999, Richardson stated, "The U.S. Government is acknowledging that we made a mistake...We need to right this wrong."

"Aside from Dixie Lee Ray, no appointee to the Department of Energy since at least 1973 has ever had any significant credentials in the nuclear field. Richardson is probably the least qualified," declares Kreisler. "It makes for sensationalism to politicize and embellish Hollywood perceptions. Too bad, since it interferes with a lot of good things that could be accomplished otherwise."

Kreisler recalls that during Governor List's administration, a blue ribbon panel was convened to look at alternate uses for the Test Site. In his opinion, one technically feasible use would have been to put in a nuclear park.

"It could supply the whole Southwest with cheap energy—but the country is so brainwashed against anything nuclear that that never has been pursued further. I think part of it is that it's a good political whipping boy. I also have a lingering suspicion that some of the energy companies are not interested in seeing nuclear power developed as long as they have oil, coal, and gas. From my vantage point, the senators, congressmen, and governors certainly can't be stupid about what they're saying. They have to know that they are twisting the facts. Like I say, it is a nice safe political theme to be anti-nuclear."

Governor Mike O'Callaghan ("a two-term governor and a very bright guy," in Kreisler's view) had shared Kreisler's support for another possible use of the site: nuclear waste storage, says Kreisler. "In the late '70s and early '80s, we weren't booming economically in Vegas. The unions were very much for it, because a minimum of one hundred million had been put aside just to get some of the infrastructure started. They had plans drawn to set up a spur rail line to take any waste coming through Nevada away from major areas like Las Vegas. It would have circumvented it totally and gone straight out to the Test Site, to be buried in casks and stored until it might be needed," Kreisler says.

He is passionate in making this point, emphasizing that "It's NOT a dump site. This is a very carefully engineered waste storage facility placed with possible retrieval of these elements to be used again in the future. One of the things people don't realize is that some of these spent fuel rods are still recyclable. The French have actually used what we call our breeder reactor technology, where they recycle the fuel right at the plant to use it again and again and again, until they have very little recyclable material left, and then they can store it—and there isn't that much, volume-wise," Kreisler maintains. He says that if Nevada had gone ahead with that, they would have had rail lines to the Test Site that could also have been used for commercial development all the way out past Indian Springs for the general public.

"We could have gotten anything the state wanted from the federal government at that time—they were very amenable. Instead, the politicians saw that it could be a very good political tool. People were very scared: you know if you don't smell it, you can't see it, you can't taste it, you get very scared of radiation. Everybody likes to believe that the Federal government is evil and ominous and all that, and this was just another nail in the government coffin."

But later, Kreisler says, after Pakistan and India set off atomic bombs, senators and congressmen suddenly turned around 180 degrees. They advocated further testing to make sure our stockpile is adequate and we can defend ourselves, says Kreisler, but as the Las Vegas and southern Nevada economy got a lot stronger, the unions were not pushing for that, as they had plenty of work in town.

"If that ever goes the other way," he states, "They will start looking for something to restart things at the Test Site. Right now, nobody cares, because the economy is so good and the building trades have more work than they know what to do with. But when the downturn comes, they'll start looking for federal dollars, and then the politicians will start talking the other way: They will start saying, 'Maybe we should put the stockpile out there.'"

For eighteen years Kreisler served as the medical director and family doctor who cared for the workers at the test site. At the end of each year, he says, he got nothing but superlative evaluations. "Because of those evaluations, REECO, Reynolds Electric and Engineering (a division of EG&G [Edgerton, Germeshausen, and Grier], a big electronic conglomerate) got extra money from the Department of Energy. My evaluations and the medical department's evaluations were probably the best of any Department of Energy installation across the country, and this was documented over and over," recalls Kreisler.

But in 1990, when a program developed by a retired admiral appointed as head of the Department of Energy during the Bush administration was put into place, Kreisler's life changed drastically.

"Admiral Watkins, in my opinion, was rather paranoid and misguided," Kreisler insists. "He developed what he called 'tiger teams' to send out to all the Department of Energy installations, to 'clean up and get everything shipshape.' On these tiger teams there were no medical people. They came out to the Nevada Test Site and they had a lot of complaints and criticisms and all that."

"At the same time," he continues, "The local Department of Energy Nevada Operations office hired a man who was a medical corpsman at Nellis and had very little practical experience. He was primarily an administrator, and he started writing up what he thought were violations of the medical program or health care delivery. He and I had big differences of opinion on many things, and I kept pointing this out to the head of the Nevada Operations office. Nobody was paying any attention. I found that I was spending ninety-five percent of my time replying to busywork which had no foundation."

As Kreisler remembers, their parent company, EG&G, was written up for about 136 alleged violations. "The man who ran the health operations over at EG&G was not a doctor, so he asked if I could help him respond to the allegations that this fellow made against EG&G. I took it home and read them, and about 128 of the 136 allegations had no basis at all. So I wrote a very, very strong critique of the whole thing as a draft and I sent a copy over to Nick Aquilina, Head of the Department of Energy Nevada Operations Office, and I gave a copy to my boss, Dale Fraiser at REECO."

Kreisler says he hoped they would look at the critique and maybe straighten out what he perceived as a bad situation. Three days after sending it, he says, he was called in on a Friday afternoon to Dale Fraiser's office and told that he was embarrassing the Department of Energy.

"I said, 'Well, am I saying anything that isn't true?' and he said, 'That's beside the point,' and I said, 'Well, what are you getting at?' and he said, 'You either resign or get fired.'"

Kreisler says he responding by saying, "The hell with you," and walked out. "I went home and I resigned. My wife got very upset and said I should have let them fire me. I said, 'The hell with the whole thing.'"

He says he did nothing until the appointment of the new Secretary of Energy Hazel O'Leary ("despite what anyone says about her, I think she was great," asserts Kreisler). Up until that time, any complaint would have gone through Nick Aquilina at the Department of Energy, the man Kreisler says was instrumental in asking for his demise.

"Now, I didn't originally know what went on behind my back, but somebody let me know that when Nick Aquilina got my draft, he became unglued. He called up Fraiser and said to get rid of me," says Kreisler. "One thing I learned when I was in the Army for two years was to keep records—and I had voluminous records as to what occurred, copies of letters I had written and all that sort of thing."

Kreisler wrote to Hazel O'Leary, who had established a Division of Employee Protection. He said he had been wrongfully terminated, even though on the record, he had resigned—but that was under duress. He says he also wrote to his senators and congressmen and started some pressure.

"I went to a local lawyer who had been with the Federal government, and he said I had no chance essentially of winning. He said, 'Go do what you can.' They sent out investigators and all that and said that I was right. They told the Department of Energy to reinstate me with back pay. They weren't interested, really, in having me out there—and frankly, I wasn't that interested in going back. So we came to an agreement and I got some extra money I hadn't planned on—plus I got the satisfaction of knowing that they had done something wrong and had to pay for it," says Kreisler. He adds, "It only took about two years and essentially on my own, without lawyers coming in until the end."

By 1990, Communist rule had come to an end and the Berlin Wall had been broken. In the wake of the end of the Cold War, atomic testing stopped. The last detonation took place in April 1991, and Congress placed a moratorium on testing in November of that year. (The comprehensive test ban treaty, sponsored by the United Nations, was signed by President Clinton in September, 1996; to date it has not been ratified by the Senate.) The testing done now at the Test Site is of the non-nuclear subcritical simulated variety. During the 1960s and early 1970s, some 10,000 workers had been employed at the site, with the number of workers peaking to 11,000 in 1992. It has now dwindled to just 2,000, Kreisler says.

Old-Fashioned Family Practice at Sea

1991–1994

ALASKA
NOVA SCOTIA
THE CARIBBEAN
THE MEDITERRANEAN

After his resignation, Kreisler found himself out of work for the first time in his career as a physician. But in 1991, he happened to spot an advertisement which would alter his professional future once again, just as the ad promoting Las Vegas had changed his life nearly twenty years earlier. While reading some medical journals in the UMC library, he came across an ad for a ship's doctor with Regent Cruise Line. He applied to the Baltimore emergency room group which took care of the medical as subcontractors, and was hired. For three years, from 1991 to 1994, he went out periodically as a cruise ship doctor on one of the five ships of the Regent Lines, sailing to Alaska, Nova Scotia, the Caribbean and the Mediterranean.

"It was a lot of fun," recalls Kreisler. "Talk about unusual experiences! That was like old-fashioned family practice at sea, with no X-ray, no lab essentially, just the nurse and me, nine hundred passengers on the big ships. They had one smaller ship that carried four hundred and then we had a crew of anywhere from three hundred to six hundred and thirty-six different nationalities. Some of them didn't speak English at all. It was interesting and a lot of fun. I didn't make any money to speak of, but I didn't want to. It was just a lot of fun and my wife could go along with me, so we had a great time."

Kreisler recalls one unusual experience he had on the smallest ship, the Regent Spirit. It went out of Jamaica, sailed six hundred miles south to Aruba, Bonaire, and Curacao and then back up again, for a week's voyage. The assistant hotel manager asked if Kreisler would see a crew member who worked in the purser's office, a young girl with some abdominal pains, says Kreisler.

"I examined her and she had some pain in the extreme right upper abdomen, which was unusual. I started questioning her and it turned out that she had gone in for an abortion in Curacao about a week or two before I had come on the ship. They had done the abortion and then when they went back, she was complaining that she wasn't feeling well. They said it was nothing but cramps," Kreisler remembers.

"In my opinion, they had probably perforated the uterus, and she now had an abscess between the liver and the diaphragm—and sure enough, that night she spiked a fever of 102°. Here we are in the middle of the Caribbean, and all I had was a limited amount of antibiotics. I started her on Rocefin IV and I told her what I thought she had and that when we got back to Jamaica, we would either fly her to Puerto Rico, her home, or we would fly her to Miami, which was the ship's major administrative area. We got her out on a plane as soon as we docked in Montego."

She went to San Juan, says Kreisler, and a couple of weeks later he got information through the hotel manager that everything had turned out well. His diagnosis had been confirmed and the patient was doing fine.

During the years he served as cruise ship physician, Kreisler recalls, there were some passengers aboard who had decided to make the voyage with the knowledge that this was their "'last cruise.' They would come on with terminal cancer, with AIDS, with all kinds of stuff. They were determined to take a cruise and, of course, some of them got very sick, and I'd usually try to stabilize them until we got into the next port. Then we got them to a local hospital or back home to their own doctors," Kreisler recalls.

Semi-Retirement

1994–1999

After sailing on his final voyage as cruise ship physician and deciding to go into semi-retirement in 1994, Kreisler applied for the position of medical director at UMC that had been created around 1966. He says there was no question in his mind that he was qualified for it—more than qualified, he adds.

"In my opinion, you needed a local person who knew the politics of the area, the interactions of the medical school, UMC, and other hospitals. So I put in my application and I think they humored me, because from the fifty that they selected initially, I came down to the last five. I was interviewed by doctors that I obviously knew. I know the doctors that torpedoed me for their personal reasons," Kreisler says. But they probably did him a favor, he adds; the man they ended up hiring at somewhere between $200,000 and $300,000 a year, plus a lot of other perks, didn't even last a year. "They got rid of him," says Kreisler, adding that it took almost another year to select a local doctor for the job.

"I didn't know if anyone would tell me any of the details, but I asked Dr. Bob Belliveau, who was very candid with me on the committee, 'What's going on?' and he said, 'You got some people that don't like you.' I said, 'I know that, but that's their problem.' He said, 'Well, they probably did you a favor not giving you the job.' I said, 'That should have been my determination.'"

Today, in retrospect, Kreisler says he thinks the medical community has lost a lot by being fragmented and extremely competitive. He makes the observation that "There are a lot of things that should be done at UMC that probably will never get done."

Not the type to go quietly into retirement—and not ready to retire completely from medicine—Kreisler is still very much involved with UMC and with the state of medicine in Las Vegas. It is his opinion that the town has gotten a little too big.

"It's still medically not cohesive. People practice on one side of the town or the other. Some of the people try to cover the whole town, which you just can't do: pediatrics, particularly, is very fragmented. I hope someday that it gets a little more cemented, now that the pediatric residency program has started at UMC," Kreisler observes.

Since 1994, Kreisler has been semi-retired; his Nevada medical license is still active and current and he does a little consulting work. Medicine is still very much a part of his life: he makes Friday grand rounds at the hospital each week and attends meetings of the tumor board on Thursdays. Since he lives in Sun City Summerlin, a retirement community, he does some advising (and acting as what he terms "medical ombudsman" for the fellow retirees).

The rest of Kreisler's time is spent enjoying tennis, gardening, saltwater fishing—"everything outdoors," he notes—writing, and enjoying the view he and wife Joan share from their comfortable suburban home. Still fit at five feet, eight inches, weighing 160 pounds, the sixty-nine year-old doctor says he is in excellent health. He still skis—though not as aggressively as he used to, particularly after breaking his leg in 1976 while skiing in Alta.

He has never regretted leaving New York for Nevada, and makes the comment that if he wants to see the fall color of turning leaves, he can see them falling off his pear tree or the nearby Arizona ash. Exhibiting the diversified tastes of typical southern Nevadans, Kreisler says he has done everything from collecting rocks in the desert, to doing exams for the Boy Scouts, to serving on the boards of the National Council of Christians and Jews and Temple Beth Shalom.

Asked if the prejudice he encountered in his younger years has lessened, Kreisler makes the statement that prejudice is still all over.

"As far as prejudice is concerned, it's probably more a little under the surface—but it'll take a millennium or more before it really might change. When things get tough, when times get bad, people tend to hit on others. I mean, look what's going on around the world: they're killing each other in Bosnia; they're killing each other in Israel, they're killing each other in Cambodia."

As far as racial prejudice in Las Vegas is specifically concerned, Kreisler says that former Governor Grant Sawyer was given the credit for breaking up prejudice against blacks on the Strip around 1960. Yet Kreisler maintains that this is not entirely accurate.

"There was a black dentist here, Dr. McMillan, who said it wasn't. Grant Sawyer went with it, and got the credit and was for it, but the guy who was really behind it was Moe Dalitz, who supposedly was with Murder Incorporated in the 1930s. Dalitz was with Meyer Lansky and all those people. He realized that hey, blacks got money, and it wouldn't be good for business if there were riots in Vegas. So he put out the word that from now on they can sleep on the Strip and do all of that—and that's what happened in 1960."

Looking back on how he has lived his life, Kreisler states what he is most proud of without a moment's hesitation: "Three wonderful kids and a nice wife." During their forty-two years together, the Kreislers raised two sons and a daughter. One son graduated from Valley High School and the other graduated from Las Vegas High School, and both went on to Reno for their undergraduate studies, then medical school at the University of Nevada School of Medicine. His eldest son, Kevin, is a psychiatrist and internist in Tucson, and Kenneth, the youngest, is part of the faculty of anesthesia for the University of West Virginia in Morgantown, West Virginia; Kreisler says Kenneth will probably move to the Southwest. The Kreislers' daughter, Kay, also graduated from Las Vegas High School and then majored in Hotel Management at the University of Nevada, Las Vegas, continuing school as an exchange student at the University of Massachusetts, from where she graduated. A writer for a convenience food magazine, Kay now lives in Phoenix.

Kreisler is also very proud of his association with the UMC Foundation, which, he says, changed health care delivery for the better—especially for the kids of Las Vegas. "As far as UMC is concerned, the work that we did set the foundation for the trauma center, pediatric outpatient, pediatric trauma, and a whole series of improvements. But the real impact on health care delivery—particularly pediatrics—was getting the foundation started." He says the UMC Foundation is still going strong— it is the proud sponsor of the statewide Nevada Day celebration with accompanying commemorative magazines—but he has not worked with the foundation since around 1992, because of his concern over possible conflict of interest situations raised by some of the board members.

As for the current state of the Test Site, Kreisler says that the drug screening program for employees he initiated in the 1980s has been discontinued because of the reduction in employees, and the practice of family-oriented care he brought to the site "has all gone by the wayside." Kreisler says there's essentially nothing going on there except for the Yucca Mountain Project, which is a relatively small work force. The

Energy Department recently announced a grant of $1.2 million, which will create a program to help find jobs for some of the thousands of Test Site workers laid off this decade. Several dozen former warehouse workers at the site are being retrained to drive big-rig trucks under the federal grant. Nevada Senator Harry Reid, who helped secure the grant, said replacing jobs will begin restoring the Test Site that had once been a "teeming city" and was vital to developing nuclear weapons from the 1950s to 1990s.

Every year at least once or more, even now, says Kreisler, there are demonstrators outside the Test Site entrance. "The crazies come out of the woodwork from various parts of the country. If you go out there and actually look at these people, they make Woodstock look like a dress event! These people come out with tents and with dilapidated motor homes. They dress rather unconventionally. I once told the Department of Energy people, 'Why don't they arrest them and get a urine sample?' I would guarantee that at least fifty percent were on some kind of illegal drug."

Nearly three decades ago, when Len Kreisler decided to adopt the city of Las Vegas as his home town, the population was around 250,000. Today, that city has changed drastically from the one he discovered. "Now, it's a mob scene downtown—it's 1.3 million now. That's more than four times. That's humongous," Kreisler observes. "But when we came out, it was a totally different life."

As to what advice he would offer doctors practicing now, Kreisler speaks up, as always. "I'd say, don't get Vegasized. Do the best job you can do. You can make a good living no matter what. Don't get tempted by the fast buck, the big kill, you know, the lights, the glamour. You can live well and take time off. Enjoy your family and take care of the patients, if that's what you went into medicine for. Now, if you went in for other reasons, you don't need to hear my philosophy. Medicine, in my opinion, is still a great calling."

This transplanted New Yorker—fully Westernized—invites all other southern Nevadans to "saddle up and ride along." As Kreisler says, "We still have a lot things to do."

Speaking Frankly: Las Vegas Health Professionals on Managed Care and Other Challenges to Modern Medicine

Gerald Joseph Sylvain, M.D., General Practitioner;
   Years Practiced: 1934–1994

Joseph Matthias George, Jr., M.D., General Practitioner;
   Years Practiced: 1940–1988

James Daniel Barger, M.D., Pathologist;
   Years Practiced: 1942–1987

Leonard Kreisler, M.D., General Practitioner; Medical Director,
   Department of Energy Atomic Testing Program: Cruise Ship
   Physician; Years Practiced: 1960–1994

With additional commentary from

Dorothy O'Donnell George, R.N., Registered Nurse;
   Medical Office Manager; Years in Nursing: 1943–1988

Gerald R. Sylvain, M.D., Ophthalmologist;
   Years Practiced: 1974–1999

America wanted cheaper health care, and that is exactly what it received from
the Wall Street health care giants. We found out that cutting costs really meant
cutting care. Today's 'McMedicine' system is akin to visiting a gourmet restau-
rant, but being allowed to order only a Big Mac—if you can even find a waiter
to serve you.

—Kazem Fathie, M.D., F.A.C.S., F.I.C.S., Immediate
Past President, Clark County Medical Society, Las Vegas, Nevada;
"Nevada Hope," letter to the editor, Vanity Fair, October 1998

Dr. Fathie's well-taken point hits the mark—and it hits home as well,
because it brings to mind a problem my own mother has with her family doctor. She is a fairly healthy eighty-six year-old who has been under
the care of the same internist for about ten years. While she feels he
cares for her health adequately for the most part, there is one aspect of
every visit that irritates her no end. As she puts it, "Dr. M. always starts
out the door before I'm done asking questions. He rushes out like he has
to catch a train."

Sound familiar? The behavior of my mother's physician is the norm
for most doctors today, who find themselves unable to devote adequate
time to each patient for many reasons.

As we enter the twenty-first century, modern medicine is poised at the
edge of a steep precipice. Managed care (see Introduction) was originally
touted as the panacea for the skyrocketing costs of health care, particularly in the areas of aging, technology, and rising expectations. It was
supposed to cut costs, streamline paperwork, and improve patient care.
But for most Americans—including my own mother and her internist—
these grand promises have not materialized. Many now view the system
as an experiment gone awry which has actually opened a Pandora's box
full of medical nightmares; in fact, there is a growing backlash against
the restrictive policies of managed care. In 1999 alone, Congress debated
patients' rights partly to curtail these policies, the American Medical
Association House of Delegates voted to form a physician union, and
Los Angeles County's non-resident physicians voted to unionize.

A stark reality of modern medicine is the rising cost of individual
health care, with even sharper spikes predicted ahead. Advocates of
managed care blame the rising tide of state and federal regulations,
which in turn raises insurers' compliance costs and boosts consumers'
insurance premiums. Consumers such as my mother are responsible for
insurance premiums, copayments, deductibles, and the portion of treatment or prescription medicines, tests, et cetera, not covered by insur-

ance. Many people—notably the elderly—are finding that they are laying out more money each month for insurance premiums and other health care costs than for housing, or for food, car insurance, life insurance, or other living costs.

Some of the other problems plaguing the populace are revealed in the following statistics:

- Since 1940, new developments in drugs and equipment have helped extend the average life span for Americans: in 1940, it was sixty-three years; in 1996, it was seventy-six.
- Three in four Americans are worried about their health care coverage.
- One in six experience delays in getting appointments.
- One-fourth can't figure out their medical bills.
- One in five has had problems paying their medical bills.
- Nearly half—forty-two percent—had to change their lives to pay the bills.
- Half worry about doctors deciding on treatment based strictly on what health plans cover.
- From 1970 to 1996, the number of health care administrators grew by 2,129 percent, while the number of doctors grew by 106.5 percent.
- Administrative costs now add up to approximately $1,000 per person.
- Nearly eight in ten physicians say that managed care has made their paperwork burden worse.
- With thousands of patients assigned to each doctor, the average office visit now lasts between seven and fifteen minutes. That includes dictating chart notes detailing each visit, reviewing and signing insurance authorizations and forms, writing out prescriptions for drugs as well as approving prescription drug refills, and consulting with other doctors, family members, and staff members of hospitals, skilled nursing facilities, et cetera.

These are statistics, and statistics are not always entirely accurate (or precise, as Dr. James Barger prefers to say). But many Americans—including the doctors interviewed below and patients such as my mother—have been affected in some way by every one of these realities.

Dr. Leonard Kreisler started off this forum, first by responding as a patient subjected to the indignities which have now become commonplace during a visit to the doctor, and next as a physician.

Leonard Kreisler, M.D. (LK): I went to see my dermatologist. I got there at 8:45 in the morning, I signed in, there were only two or three people in the waiting room—but I didn't get in until 10:00. He sprayed some liquid nitrogen, and I was out—in fifteen minutes or less. You go in, you take your shirt off, you're standing there freezing, waiting for him to come in—it's hard to put up with it.

But he's got to support a lifestyle that he thinks he's entitled to—or his family thinks he's entitled to. He gets carried away with money and glitz, and the practice of medicine takes a back seat to a jet-set style of life.

Gerald R. Sylvain, M.D. (GRS): If you get caught up in all that, I think that's really true. You strap yourself not only into a business overhead because of running your office, but you also get caught up in a lifestyle that's beyond what you might normally have. My exposure to medicine is the medicine that my dad practiced. I think that's a medicine that I wish we didn't get away from. I've been fortunate in that I've been able to practice mostly that way. If I have to have a patient sit down in front of me and think dollar signs to make it work, then somehow I'm missing the boat, and I hope it never comes to that. People say, "Well, don't you know your insurance? Don't you know how much you charge?" I don't know any of that stuff. I mean, I know my staff is supposed to know that—I'm not totally ignorant, I have some sense of it. But it's not a thing that runs my life, though I think it is for a lot of doctors. It's too bad.

Joseph George, Jr., M.D. (JG): Doctors of my vintage have had many discussions about how medicine has changed during the time we practiced, and we universally felt that we'd practiced medicine in the golden era of medicines. We universally dislike the current way that medicine is practiced with the emphasis on HMOs (health maintenance organizations, one type of managed care) and the restrictions that doctors are under, time-wise, in seeing patients. You can't do a decent job in seeing and taking care of people in ten or twelve minutes per person—and some of them require that you see five people an hour. This averages out to twelve minutes each, which includes dictations, etc. That, in turn, means that the time is not spent with the patients, really. Over at Southwest Medical Associates, the general physicians have to see five patients an hour, which comes down to twelve minutes per patient. Subtract any bathroom time if you have to go or whatever, you have to dictate as you go along, and of course you do your prescriptions, and all the other things, out of that twelve minutes—you can't do a decent job on that basis. You just can't.

GRS: I don't do that. I don't belong to any of that stuff (managed care organizations). I'm still practicing my dad's kind of medicine. I don't survive well. But I think there's an inner satisfaction I have that a lot of doctors maybe don't have. Monetarily it's not rewarding—I think I probably make the least amount of money for all the ophthalmologists here. But I think in the end I've been fortunate, personally, because I feel I'm practicing more of the old style that we never should have gotten away from, that we were forced to get away from.

James D. Barger, M.D. (JB): Everybody seemed to be more relaxed in those days, and I think they should go back to having some County Society medical meetings—let people know each other, just get together. We used to have a pathology society, too; we would meet about once every three months and have dinner. That was kind of fun in those days. I think you ought to bring those days back. I don't know—people are too busy nowadays for that, I guess.

LK: One urologist supposedly told a patient friend of mine that he sees forty to forty-five patients a day. My friend said, "Yeah, and he only spent five minutes with me." You cannot see forty-five patients a day and do a good job. You just can't. Consequently, in certain specialties, when people have trouble, I recommend they go out of town. Patients who'd had their prostates taken out here, were impotent, couldn't get a straight answer from the doctor, I'd send them down to the Mayo Clinic extension in Scottsdale. He'd run through all the tests, spend one to two to three hours with them, literally, explain all their options, what the problems were, the whole thing. It's one-third the price, and they were happy with the follow-up. And if even if he couldn't do anything for them, they came back happy. I couldn't find people to do that in this town.

GRS: I think the transition and changeover is here (managed care has replaced the traditional "fee for service" care in which the patient can see any doctor or use any hospital; the patient pays the doctor then waits for insurance company reimbursement). I'm lucky because I'm in a big city that's growing fantastically, so I've always had a certain number of patients. I think most of the reason I get patients is word of mouth, which is what I think you should get them from. If you have somebody come in to see you that wants to come in because they heard something, that starts you off on a good foot, rather than maybe seeing an ad.

JG: There are many more things that can be done today for a person, medically—but from the standpoint of the people being taken care of, a lot of patients are very unhappy with their medical care because the doctors don't really build a relationship.

Gerald J. Sylvain, M.D. (GJS): I enjoyed the practice of medicine immensely in those days—I don't think I'd enjoy it now. We had patients that we became very friendly with, and we really looked after them. Now in this day and age, they all belong to something and they go where they're told to go—they have no choice to pick doctors. There isn't that same feeling anymore.

JG: The malpractice rates have increased a great deal, to a considerable extent, because the doctors don't build a bond with the patient. They don't explain things well. As a consequence, the suits have many times been blamed on people just not having a feeling of any positive care by the doctor. They wonder if he couldn't have done more, or whether he couldn't have given them different medicine. If a patient had a reaction to the medicine, he wonders, "Did he give me the right medicine?" This is a tremendous disadvantage whereas in the old days we knew our patients so well. Even if they had a reaction to the medication they would call you on the phone and explain, and then you would change it and there wouldn't be any hard feeling at all.

LK: There's a big quandary on the patient's side of whom to go see. They're very annoyed with some of the charges, lack of communication, lack of consistency, etc. A lot of these things are valid. As a result, when the outcome is not what they expect, they start looking for remedies which start involving litigation and accusation and all that sort of thing. I think the patients lose a lot by not having a family doctor that they can relate to. On the other hand, a lot of these people coming in are from big cities and are very specialist-oriented. If they don't have a straightforward or easy diagnosis right away, they request a specialist, so you know, the family doctor, sooner or later, gets the feeling, "What am I?" So I think it works both ways. You have less patient loyalty and you have less doctor attention and commitment. It's very unfortunate.

JG: I don't think there's the slightest bit of question about there being a difference in the public's attitude towards doctors since I began practicing. We have some excellent doctors here, but oftentimes they are limited in the amount of time they can spend with a patient. Patients are seeing more and more shows on TV where the doctor sits and talks to them at length and helps them with all sorts of social problems and all sorts of things. They think they should have that too. They are just not going to get it with the present setup. Real life is not like what they see on TV.

LK: It's not only managed care. The biggest argument I have with managed care—the philosophy of managed care to me is very good. But in actual experience the thing that bothers me is that top management keeps getting higher and higher salaries, but the salaries don't trickle down to the guys and the women who are doing the work in the front line, nor does the quality of patient care get any better. When a CEO (chief executive officer) gets four or five million and up, I don't understand that—managed care is supposed to be saving money. Their prices are starting to go up. Why are these horrific salaries being paid? I tell our two sons, who are doctors now, that medicine has gotten more expensive; probably less personal and not necessarily that much better. I've heard some of the local doctors say that fifty percent is going toward overhead—office salaries, management, insurance, the whole ball of wax. People who go into family practice today don't do as wide a range of things; the malpractice fees are just too high, and they don't get paid. Even now, in today's paper it said Nevada is number one in hospital costs by forty percent.

Dorothy O'Donnell George, R.N. (DG): Just recently we had a friend who was in the hospital here. I won't mention the hospital, but she was there for six days after lung surgery and didn't have a change of bed linen the whole time she was there. That would have not been tolerated at all when I was in nursing. That was just not even thought of. It's sad, really. She happened to have her sister here, who is not a nurse but was there helping her, and without her sister I don't know if she would have survived the surgery, actually. She had helped her get up and move around and do all the things that normally nurses would have done. I think it's very much a trend. Unless nursing schools go back to teaching bedside nursing, I don't think there's going to be very many nurses. Most people you talk to talk about the poor nursing care they got while they were at the hospital, and I've always told Joe (Joseph M. George, Jr., M.D., Dorothy's husband), "Don't take me to the hospital if I get sick. I'll die at home." To me, hospitals would profit more if the patients have a good rapport with the hospital. They can tell other people how great the hospital was and what great care they received. I would not want to be a nurse in today's world, but the way it was when I entered nursing school I certainly would. I think the nursing profession has to change from the top and the medical profession has to assist them, working together as a team.

JB: I remember when Las Vegas was a growing town with a medical group that was not very big. I knew everybody. We had frequent meetings. You got to know everybody and it was very congenial, a thing that I miss now. You got together and people got to know each other. I think a lot of that led to consultations—anyway, people were more congenial.

LK: I was fortunate in about 1985 to have attended a medical meeting in Dallas, at which Wilbur Cohn was one of the major speakers. He was actually the guy that was the father of Medicare and his statement was that he thought that medicine cycled every thirty years as far as its structure was concerned. He thought that by the 1990s there would be three types of medicine. There would be the old traditional fee for service, for those that have the money and can pay for it; you'll have the managed care type of health service; and then you'll have the Medicare/Medicaid indigent group— and it looks like that's the way it's sorted out. They'll each have their components, and they'll seesaw back and forth. I think now it's going to be a struggle between those three to see how it's going to balance out. I think it's still in a big state of flux. But the patient gets the short end of the stick—and you don't save money, because CEOs (of managed care organizations) want to get big salaries.

While the people of Las Vegas—and all throughout the country—are waiting to see how the health care system sorts itself out, the dilemma continues. Many managed care organizations keep on denying as much care as possible to cut costs: the battle plays itself out every day, almost as if managed care organizations are waging war against patients and doctors. In the meantime, patients need to think about when—if at all— they've been able to see the same doctor twice in a row; when their doctor took the time with them they felt they needed; and why they feel frustrated with confusing insurance company regulations and billing practices. A groundswell of dissatisfaction is building among doctors. When the ranks of patients whose health is often being compromised by the insurance industry band together with their physicians, it can signal a new, yet comfortingly familiar, standard: a return to good medicine.

About the Doctors Mentioned
Throughout This Book

The biographical information that follows was provided by Anton P. Sohn, M.D., founder and chief historian of University of Nevada Great Basin History of Medicine Program and Pathology Department chair, University of Nevada School of Medicine, Reno. Dr. Sohn is also the author of a number of books on the history of medicine.

The doctors' names are organized according to which part of the book they appear in and are alphabetized by last names.

Part 1: Gerald Joseph Sylvain, M.D.

Wilmer Lars Allen: Allen, born in Utah in 1907, graduated from the University of Utah in 1929 and the University of Pennsylvania Medical College in 1932. Board certified in otolaryngology, Allen served in the U.S. Army from 1942 to 1946. He practiced in Provo, Utah, before coming to Las Vegas in 1946; he was president of the Clark County Medical Society in 1951.

Frederick Mather Anderson: Anderson is recognized as the father of the University of Nevada medical school. A native-born Nevadan, he was born in 1906, graduated from Ely High School in 1923, and graduated from the University of Nevada in Reno in 1928. After three years as a Rhodes Scholar at Oxford, England, he attended Harvard Medical School. He was licensed in 1937 and practiced in Carson City, and from 1941 to 1946, Dr. Anderson served in the U. S. Army. After the war he returned to Nevada and practiced as a surgeon in Reno. President of the Nevada State Medical Association in 1955, he was a Regent of the University of Nevada in 1957. Dr. Anderson was instrumental in the formation of the University of Nevada School of Medicine.

Raymond B. Balcom: Balcom graduated from the University of Nebraska School of Medicine in 1920 and came to Nevada in 1930. He served on the Board of Medical Examiners and later retired in Ontario, California.

Ralph Alvin Bowdle: Bowdle was born in 1884 and graduated from the Medical College of Ohio in 1809. He was licensed in Steptoe, Nevada in 1916. He served on the Nevada State Board of Medical Examiners and was president of the Nevada State Medical Association in 1921 and 1922. He died in 1943.

David Decatur Carr: Born in 1898 in Tennessee, Carr received his M.D. from Vanderbilt School of Medicine in 1928. He moved to Las Vegas in 1949, where he practiced public health and preventative medicine. He died in 1973.

Jack Cherry: Jack C. Cherry was born in 1898 and received his M.D. from the Kansas City College of Medicine in 1920. After practicing in Montana, he was licensed in Tonopah, Nevada in 1924, then moved to Goldfield, Nevada, a few years later. In 1942 Dr. Cherry became the administrator and county physician for Clark County General Hospital in Las Vegas (later renamed University Medical Center of Southern Nevada), a position he held for many years.

John Clement Cowden: Cowden, born in 1864, received his medical degree from the Pacific Coast Regular College of Medicine in 1900. Licensed in Nevada in 1905, Dr. Cowden practiced in Tonopah from 1906 to 1927.

Robert Russell Craig: Awarded his medical degree in 1911 from the University of Minnesota, Craig was born in Canada in 1882. From 1912 to 1918 he served as chief surgeon of various Nevada mining companies in Fairview, Buckhorn, Aurora, Goldfield, and Tonopah. He specialized in industrial medicine and was president of the Nevada State Medical Association in 1929. Dr. Craig died in 1952.

Dale Hadfield: A 1942 graduate of the Kentucky School of Medicine,

Hadfield was born in Utah in 1916. In 1946 he was licensed in Elko, Nevada, and later moved to Tacoma, Washington.

Edward Everett Hamer: Hamer was born in Pennsylvania in 1877, and received his medical degree from the University of Kentucky School of Medicine in 1906. Dr. Hamer moved to Carson City in 1919, and from 1927 to 1936 was the Nevada State Health Officer. He served on the state Board of Medical Examiners from 1926 to 1940 and was president of the Nevada State Medical Association in 1935. He died in Carson City in 1946.

Stanley Laird Hardy: Born in Utah in 1906, Hardy graduated from the University of Utah in 1930 and from Rush Medical College in 1933. Dr. Hardy was licensed in Nevada in 1933 and practiced in Overton, Nevada in 1935. After moving to Las Vegas, he served as a member of the Nevada State Board of Medical Examiners, president of Clark County Medical Society (in 1945), and president of the Nevada State Medical Association in 1957. Hardy died on March 14, 1976.

Arthur James Hood: Hood, born in Battle Mountain, Nevada in 1895, graduated from the University of Nevada in Reno and the Stanford University School of Medicine. He was licensed in Elko, Nevada in 1921, where he practiced until his 1956 retirement.

Daniel Joseph Hurley: Hurley, born in Idaho in 1902, graduated in medicine from Creighton University and received his Masters in Public Health from Harvard. Beginning in 1928, he practiced in Eureka, Nevada, until World War II when he was in the U.S. Navy Reserve. In 1948 he moved to Carson City and became the state health officer. He died in 1973.

Richard Henry Laub: A native Nevadan, Laub was born in 1911 and graduated from St. Louis University School of Medicine in 1943. He was licensed in Nevada in 1947 and died in 1988.

Dana Duncan Little: Little was born in Nebraska in 1910 and received his M.D. from the University of Southern California in 1938. He practiced in Boulder City, Nevada for a year and a half before moving north to Reno, Nevada where he did general practice and surgery. *See* William Morris Little, his younger brother.

William Morris Little: A 1938 graduate of the University of Southern California, Little was born in Nebraska in 1919. He was licensed in Reno, Nevada in 1938, where he practiced obstetrics and gynecology. From 1940 to 1942 Dr. Little was the director of the state health department's maternal and child health division, before going to work in Manzanar, where he was in charge of the Japanese evacuation center hospital.

Grant Lund: Lund was born in 1905 and graduated from the University of Maryland Medical School in 1936. He was licensed in Nevada and registered in Las Vegas in 1946.

John Riley McDaniel, Jr.: McDaniel was born in Mississippi in 1900. He attended the University of Mississippi then graduated from the New York University of Medicine medical school in 1924. After practicing a few years in Blytheville, Arkansas, he came to Las Vegas in 1931. He served in the U.S. Army from 1942–45. He was president of the Nevada State Medical Association in 1946.

Royce W. "Roy" Martin: Considered to be Las Vegas' most important pre-World War II doctor, Martin was born in Nebraska in 1874. He graduated from the University of Kansas City Medical College in 1903 and was licensed in Nevada in 1905. Elected to the state assembly in 1923, Martin built Las Vegas Hospital, which was for years the city's only hospital; it opened on December 31, 1937. He died in Henderson, Nevada in 1943.

Leslie Arthur Moren: Moren, born in Wisconsin in 1914, graduated from the University of Minnesota Medical School in 1938. That same year he was licensed in Elko, Nevada, where he practiced until he entered the U.S. Army in 1942. He has served on the state Board of Medical Examiners, was president of the Nevada State Medical Association, and for fifteen years was the state's representative to the American Medical Association. *See* Owen Bolstad, *Leslie Moren, Fifty Years an Elko County Doctor* (Reno: University of Nevada Oral History Program, 1992).

George Francis Pierrot: Pierrot, born in Missouri in 1861, graduated from St. Louis College of Physicians and Surgeons in 1890. He moved to Goldfield, Nevada, in 1929.

Otto Ravenholt: He was born in Wisconsin in 1927 and graduated from the University of Minnesota School of Medicine in 1958. After serving in the U.S. Army from 1947 to 1952, he obtained his Masters in Public Health in 1960. Dr. Ravenholt worked in Topeka, Kansas until 1964, when he came to Nevada. The director of the Clark County Health Department for thirty-six years, he served as director of the Nevada Department of Health and Human Services under Governor Robert Laxalt. Dr. Ravenholt has also served as administrator of Southern Nevada Memorial Hospital (now University Medical Center of Southern Nevada) and Clark County coroner. He retired in 1999.

William Bee Ririe: Ririe, born in West China in 1896, graduated from the University of Toronto School of Medicine in 1928. He came to East Ely, Nevada in 1930 and practiced there and in Ely. The White Pine County Hospital is named in his honor. He died in 1976.

Robert Peter Roantree: Roantree was born in Iowa in 1895. He received his M.D. from Washington University in St. Louis, Missouri in 1919. Dr. Roantree moved to Ely, Nevada in 1920 and practiced in Elko. He was on the state Board of Medical Examiners and was president of the Nevada State Medical Association in 1931. He practiced in Elko, Nevada until his death in 1950.

Charles Edgar Secor: Born in Michigan in 1882, Secor graduated from Wisconsin College of Physicians and Surgeons in 1905 and was licensed in Cherry Creek, Nevada in 1908. He moved to Tuscarora, Nevada in 1914 and later moved to Elko, Nevada. Secor was president of the Nevada State Medical Association in 1937.

Hale B. Slavin: Slavin was born in Mississippi in 1906 and graduated from Iowa University School of Medicine in 1930. Licensed in Nevada in 1933, Dr. Slavin practiced in Las Vegas for many years. He was on the Board of Medical Examiners and president of the Clark County Medical Society from 1951 to 1952. He served in the U.S. Navy from 1944 to 1946 and from 1950 to 1951.

Noah Smernoff: Smernoff was born in Colorado in 1904 and graduated from the University of Colorado School of Medicine in 1928. Noah was licensed in McGill, Nevada in 1930 and practiced there until 1953 when he moved to Reno, where he lives today. *See* R.T. King, *Noah Smernoff, A Life in Medicine* (Reno: University of Nevada Oral History Program, 1990).

Kenneth Franklin Smith: Born in Oregon in 1906, Smith graduated from Ohio State University School of Medicine in 1930. He practiced in New York City for eight years before joining the U.S. Navy in 1943. After the war, in 1946, Dr. Smith was licensed in Reno before coming to Las Vegas.

Zigmunt Melvin Starzynski: Starzynski, born in Pennsylvania in 1911, graduated from the University of Pittsburgh School of Medicine in 1943. He was in the U.S. Army before settling in Las Vegas in 1946, where he specialized in tuberculosis and psychiatry.

Gerald R. Sylvain: Sylvain was born in Nevada in 1941. A 1967 graduate of Marquette University Medical School, Sylvain has practiced ophthalmology in Las Vegas since 1974.

James Thom: Thom was born in Indiana in 1890. He graduated from Indiana University School of Medicine in 1918, and after training in radiology practiced in Clarksdale, Arizona and Sacramento, California. He was licensed in Reno, Nevada in 1929 and practiced radiology and industrial medicine in Carson City and in Ormsby County, Nevada. He died in 1962.

Theodore Thorpe: Born in 1941, he graduated from medical school in Argentina in 1971. Since 1975 he has practiced family medicine in Las Vegas.

Claire Watson Woodbury: Woodbury was born in Utah in 1895 and graduated from George Washington University in Washington D.C. in 1923. Dr. Woodbury was licensed in Nevada in 1923 and then practiced in Las Vegas.

Part 2: Joseph Matthias George, Jr., M.D.

Wilmer Lars Allen: *see* Part One: Gerald Joseph Sylvain, M.D.

Frederick Mather Anderson: *see* Part One: Gerald Joseph Sylvain, M.D.

Harold Lester Boyer: Boyer, born in Arkansas in 1916, obtained his medical degree from the University of Oklahoma in 1941. During World

War II he was in the U.S. Navy Reserve. He studied dermatology and practiced in Birmingham, Alabama, before coming to Las Vegas in 1952, where he limited his practice to dermatology.

Emil Francis Cava: Cava was born in California in 1921 and received his medical degree from the University of California, San Francisco in 1948. Licensed in Nevada in 1948, he limited his practice to obstetrics and gynecology.

Jack Cherry: *see* Part One: Gerald Joseph Sylvain, M.D..

Harry E. Fightlin: Born in New York in 1909, Fightlin graduated from Long Island College of Medicine in 1934. He was licensed to practice in Reno before coming to Las Vegas.

Stanley Laird Hardy: *see* Part One: Gerald Joseph Sylvain, M.D.

Chester Clinton Lockwood: Lockwood was born in Oklahoma in 1911 and obtained his medical degree from Northwestern University in 1936. After serving in the U.S. Army from 1942 to 1946, he was licensed in Reno in 1946. He later moved to Las Vegas, where he practiced EENT (eye, ear, nose and throat).

Grant Lund: *see* Part One: Gerald Joseph Sylvain, M.D.

Donald Maxwell MacCornack: Born in Illinois in 1897, he obtained his medical degree from the University of Illinois School of Medicine in 1926. He practiced in South America and Gallup, New Mexico until 1942, when he moved to Boulder City. During the second World War he served in the U.S. Marine Corps. He was a president of the Clark County Medical Society. (*See* his brother, below.)

Eugene Andrew MacCornack: E. A. MacCornack was born in Illinois in 1886. In 1913 he obtained his medical degree from the University of Illinois School of Medicine. He practiced in Boulder City in 1944, but later moved to Warrenton, Virginia.

John Riley McDaniel, Jr.: *see* Part One: Gerald Joseph Sylvain, M.D.

Otto Ravenholt: *see* Part One: Gerald Joseph Sylvain, M.D.

Kenneth Franklin Smith: *see* Part One: Gerald Joseph Sylvain, M.D.

Claire Watson Woodbury: *see* Part One: Gerald Joseph Sylvain, M.D.

Part 3: James Daniel Barger, M.D.

Jurgens H. Bauer: Born in 1913 in Brooklyn, he received his M.D. from Long Island College of Medicine in 1939 and practiced as a Syracuse orthopedic surgeonfrom 1944 until 1960. While in private practice in Las Vegas, Bauer was Southern Nevada Memorial Hospital chief of orthopedics, served on the Governor's Committee for Employment of the Handicapped from 1975 to 1978, and received the state medical association president's citation in 1979. He died in 1980.

Robert Rock Belliveau: Belliveau was born in Massachusetts in 1932 and received his M.D. from Washington University School of Medicine in St. Louis, Missouri in 1957. He was on active duty in the U.S. Air Force from 1960 to 1963, when he was licensed in Nevada in pathology.

Robert Brown: Born in Montana in 1932, Brown obtained his Medical degree from Baylor University in Houston. He was licensed in Carson City in 1964 and has been a longtime family practitioner. A past president of the Nevada State Medical Association, Brown was Nevada's delegate to the American Medical Association (AMA) for many years.

John Grayson: Grayson was born in Ohio in 1932 and graduated from Washington University School of Medicine, St. Louis, Missouri in 1957. He was licensed in Las Vegas in 1965 and practiced pathology. Dr. Grayson later retired from medicine to run for mayor of Las Vegas on the Libertarian ticket.

Bob Horn: Robert C. Horn, Jr., M.D., was president of the College of American Pathologists (CAP) from 1973 to 1975.

Larry McCormack: Lawrence J. McCormack, M.D. served as College of American Pathologists president from 1979 to 1981.

Bill Reals: From 1971 to 1973, William J. Reals was president of the College of American Pathologists.

Willis M. Russell: Russell, born in 1931, graduated from Tulane University School of Medicine in 1958. He was licensed In Nevada in 1968 in pathology.

Ronald Slaughter: Dr. Slaughter graduated from the University of Chicago School of Medicine in 1967. He then served four years in the U.S. Navy. He was licensed in Nevada in 1975 and has practiced pathology at Sunrise Hospital.

Henry B. Soloway: Soloway was born in 1936 and graduated from the State University College of Medicine in New York City in 1961. He was licensed in Nevada in 1970 in pathology.

Part 4: Leonard Kreisler, M.D.

Savino "Beanie" Cavender: Born in 1913 in Wakefield, Michigan, he served the military for 27 years, retiring as a colonel in 1939. In 1967 he moved to Las Vegas, joining Reynolds Electrical and Engineering Company as a physician and assistant medical director. An expert in the medical effects of radiation and nuclear weapons testing at the Nevada Test Site, he served as medical advisor to the Atomic Energy Commission and to the Department of Energy's test controller. He died at the age of 68.

Robert Rock Belliveau: *see* Part Three: James Daniel Barger.

Thorne Jefferson Butler: Butler was born in Hawaii in 1929 and graduated from Stanford University School of Medicine in 1955. After serving for ten years in the U.S. Air Force, he was licensed in Nevada in 1966 and practiced pathology. He died about eight years ago.

Neil Carmena: Neil Carmena was born in Louisiana in 1932. In 1956 he graduated from Louisiana State University School of Medicine. He was licensed in Nevada in 1963 and is still practicing internal medicine in Las Vegas.

Jack Cherry: *see* Part One: Gerald Joseph Sylvain, M.D.

Louis Friedman: Born in New York in 1914, he received his M.D. from the University of Arkansas. He was licensed in Nevada in 1970 and practiced internal medicine at Sunrise Hospital in Las Vegas. He died in 1995.

Elias Ghanem: Ghanem graduated from Duke University School of Medicine in 1970 and came to Las Vegas in 1973. He specializes in family practice.

Pablo Joya: He was born in 1944 in Honduras. Joya graduated from National University in Mexico in 1969 and was licensed in Nevada in 1977. He still practices internal medicine in Las Vegas.

Joseph Kaufman: Kaufman graduated form Loyola University School of Medicine in 1969 and has been in Las Vegas since 1978. He practices cardiology.

Stephen Kollins: Kollins graduated from the University of Cincinnati College of Medicine in 1969 and came to Las Vegas in 1973.

Harry Knudson: Harris W. Knudson was born in 1929 and graduated from the University of Minnesota School of Medicine in 1955. After completing his residency in radiology , he served in the U.S. Air Force from 1961 to 1964, when he moved to Las Vegas and practiced at Southern Nevada Memorial Hospital. He served as president of the Clark County Medical Society and of the Nevada State Medical Association, and was voted the Distinguished Physician of the Year in 1985 by the Nevada State Medical Association. He died in 1985.

Enrique Lacayo: Born in Nicaragua in 1943, Lacayo received his medical degree from the University of New Mexico School of Medicine in 1969. He was licensed to practice medicine in Las Vegas in 1976.

Tony Marlon: Marlon was born in 1942 and received his M.D. from the State University of New York School of Medicine in Brooklyn in 1967. He was licensed to practice cardiology in Las Vegas in 1972.

Ivan Mindlin: Mindlin was born in Canada in 1929 and graduated from the University of Manitoba School of Medicine in 1955. He became licensed in Nevada in 1958.

Joseph Quagliana: Quagliana received his M.D. from the State University of New York at Buffalo in 1959 and was licensed in Las Vegas in 1974. He practices oncology (the study and practice of treating tumors).

Edward Quinn: Quinn was born in 1943 and received his medical degree from Creighton University School of Medicine in 1969. He was licensed in Nevada in 1974 and has practiced in Las Vegas specializing in cardiology.

Bibliography

Anderson, Kenneth N. and Anderson, Lois E. *Mosby's Pocket Dictionary of Medicine, Nursing, and Allied Health*, Third Edition, (St. Louis: Mosby, Inc., 1998).

Benet, William Rose, Ed. *The Reader's Encyclopedia* (New York: Thomas Y. Crowell Company, 1948).

Chapman, Robert L., Ph.D. *American Slang* (New York: Harper & Row, Publishers, Inc., 1987).

Clark County Medical Society 1999 Directory of Physicians (Las Vegas: Clark County Medical Society, 1999).

Clark County Medical Society Archives.

Cudek, Phyllis. "The Hospitals of Clark County: Development of Medicine in a Rapidly Growing Nevada Community." *Greasewood Tablettes*, Vol. VII, No. 4. Reno, Nevada: Department of Pathology, Great Basin History of Medicine Division, University of Nevada School of Medicine, Winter 1996–1997.

"Dr. Jack C. Cherry: A Nevada Pioneer." *Nevada Health Review*, July 1981.

Dunteman, Dana. "Dr. Sylvain Slowing Down—Slightly." *Las Vegas Sun*, May 26, 1992.

Earl, Phillip E. "Las Vegas' Forgotten Physician: Dr. Roy W. Martin." *Greasewood Tablettes*, Vol. IX, No. 3. Reno, Nevada: Department of Pathology, Great Basin History of Medicine Division, University of Nevada School of Medicine, Fall 1998.

Evans, K.J. "Roy Martin: The Driven Doctor." *Las Vegas Review-Journal*, February 7, 1999.

"Federal Grant to Convert Nuclear Workers into Truck Drivers." *Reno Gazette-Journal* (Associated Press), September 10, 1999.

Gordon, Suzanne. "Even if the Doctors Are in They Can't See You Now." Opinion Page, *Reno Gazette-Journal*, July 11, 1999.

Hebert, H. Josef. "Feds Admit that Nuclear Workers Were Made Sick." *Reno Gazette-Journal* (Associated Press), July 16, 1999.

Hirsch, Jr., E.D.; Kett, Joseph F.; Trefil, James. *The Dictionary of Cultural Literacy: What Every American Needs to Know* (Boston: Houghton Mifflin Company, 1988).

Hulse, James W. *Forty Years in the Wilderness: Impressions of Nevada 1940–1980* (Reno: University of Nevada, Reno Press, 1986).

Kahn, Charles N. "Managed Care Means Lower Costs." Opposing View, Editorial Page, *USA Today*, March 2, 1999.

Kreisler, Len. "Len Kreisler: A Medical Gain for Nevada." *Nevada Day , Vol. 4, 1864–1989: 125 Years of Vision.* Las Vegas: University Medical Center Foundation, 1989.

Martin, Elizabeth, Ed. *The Bantam Medical Dictionary* (New York: Bantam Books, 1981).

Mazzarella, David, Ed. "Pity the Poor Patient, Buried in Piles of Health-Care Paperwork." Our View, Editorial Page, *USA Today*, March 2, 1999.

Nevada Board of Medical Examiners Records.

Nevada Day, Vol. VII, 1864–1991. Las Vegas: University Medical Center Foundation, 1991.

Nevada Historical Society Archives, Museum Collection, and Research Library.

Nevada State Library Archives.

Nevada State Medical Association Records.

Patterson, Edna B. *Sagebrush Doctors* (Springville, Utah: Art City Publishing Company, 1972).

Photography Collection, Nevada Historical Society, Reno, Nevada.

Puleo, Lisa. "James D. Barger, M.D. Oral History (unpublished)." Department of Pathology, Great Basin History of Medicine Division, University of Nevada School of Medicine, Reno, Nevada, 1998.

Puleo, Lisa. "Joseph M.George, Jr., M.D. Oral History" (unpublished). Department of Pathology, Great Basin History of Medicine Division, University of Nevada School of Medicine, Reno, Nevada, 1998.

Puleo, Lisa. "Leonard Kreisler, M.D. Oral History" (unpublished). Department of Pathology, Great Basin History of Medicine Division, University of Nevada School of Medicine, Reno, Nevada, 1998.

Reference Desk, Washoe County Library, Downtown Reno/Main Branch.

Ross, Silas E. *A Directory of Nevada Medical Practitioners Past and Present.* Reno: Private Printing, 1957.

Rothenberg, Robert E., M.D., F.A.C.S. *Medical Dictionary and Health Manual.* New York: Signet/NAL Penguin, 1988.

Russell, Diane. "Building Fire Robs Las Vegas of Piece of History." *Las Vegas Review-Journal,* February, 1988.

Sion, Michael. *Staying Power: Eight Nevadanas Over 80 Share Secrets for a Life of Health, Happiness and Fulfillment.* Reno: Published by Countess Angela Dandini, 1997.

Sohn, Anton Paul. *The Healers of 19th Century Nevada: A Compendium of Medical Practitioners.* Reno: Greasewood Press, 1997.

Sohn, Anton Paul. *Hospital Builder: Quincy E. Fortier, A Nevada Physician* (unpublished). Reno: Greasewood Press, 1996.

Sohn, Anton Paul."Gerald J. Sylvain, M.D. Oral History," (unpublished). Department of Pathology, Great Basin History of Medicine Division, University of Nevada School of Medicine, Reno, Nevada, 1998.

Stewart, Doug. "This Joint Is Jumping." *Smithsonian,* Vol. 29 No.12, March 1999.

Sunrise Hospital Community Services.

University Medical Center of Southern Nevada Community Services.

"Vegas Doctor Top Pathologist." *Valley Times,* October 18, 1977.

Vital Statistics, *Las Vegas Review-Journal,* 1980, 1981.

"What's It Mean?" Gannett News Service, *Reno Gazette-Journal,* July 11, 1999.

Winston's New and Complete Atlas of the World. Philadelphia: The John C. Winston Company,1927.

Wright, Dorothy. "Yesterday." *The Nevadan,* May 11, 1986.

Index

adm. Las Vegas Hosp. & Clinic, 41
EG&G, 156
El Rancho Vegas, 29, 81
Eliason, Dr. Eldridge
 Barger instructor, 96
Elks Club Building.
 See Sylvain's Goldfield office
Esmeralda Co. Hosp., 19
Esmeralda Co. Physician
 politics, 21
Evashevski, Forest
 Univ. Mich. & Univ. Iowa football, 24

F
Fahey, Kay, xi
Fathie, Dr. Kazem
 past pres. Clark Co. Med. Soc., 166
FDA, 57
Ferguson, Dr. F.M.
 formed Las Vegas Hosp. Found., 32
Fightlin, Dr. Harry, 74
 bio., 181
Flamingo, The, 81
Flangas, Bill, 144
 engineer, 139
 UMC Found., 145
Fouts, Jr., Dr. Joe, 109, 110
 Good Samaritan Hosp. path., 108
 Sunrise Hosp. path., 108
Fraiser, Dale, 157
 REECO, 156
Franklin, George
 Clark Co. commisioner, 26
Fremont, The, 30
Friedman, Dr. Louis
 bio., 183
 internist, 135

G
Gardner, Dr. Gawinn, 41
Garrison, Teresa, xi
Gavin, Father
 Goldfield priest, 18
George, 3rd, Joseph
 son, 58, 87
George, Dorothy, xii
 less nursing care, 171, 172

wife, 77
George, Dr. June
 adopted daughter, 87.
 See June George
George, Janelle
 adopted daughter, 81, 87
George, Jr., Dr. Joseph M., xii, 2, 51
 advice to doctors, 87
 AMA member, 74
 Amer. Legion, 85
 arrives in Las Vegas, 62
 Bd. of Med. Examiners, 80
 chief of staff of UMC, 76
 Child Welfare Bd., 75
 Elks, 85
 examiner FAA, 75
 family, 52
 flight school, 58
 HMOs limit phys., 168
 Hixson Award, 86
 Juvenile Probation Bd., 75
 Knights of Columbus, 86
 Las Vegas office schedule, 68
 malpractice insurance, 79
 malpractice rate, 170
 med. influenced by TV, 171
 Nev. Living Treasure in Rehab.
  Award, 83
 Nev. Nat. Guard, 75
 Nev. State Med. Assoc. Commu-
  nity Ser. Award, 83
 obstetrics practice, 71
 office economics, 71
 patients, 72
 practice in Sudlersville, 56
 Praeceptor Carissimus Award by
  Univ. Nev. School of Med., 84
 pres. Amer. Acad. Family Phy., 74
 pres. Clark Co. Med. Soc., 67
 pres. Kiwanis Club, 81
 pres. Nev. State Nev. Assoc., 75
 state commander VFW, 75
 Sudlersville High School, 53
 Tampa-St. Petersburg, 60
 unhappy patients, 170
 Univ. Md. internship, 55
 Univ. Md. Med. School, 54

pneumonia treatment in Goldfield
pigeon poultice, 19
pneumothorax
TB treatment, 37, 57
polio
Goldfield, 22
iron lung, 37
polychlorinated biphenyls
toxic fumes at Area 51, 152
potassium permanganate
treatment for gonorrhea, 22
Potter, Bob
Barger chief tech, 113
prostitutes
George patients, 72
Sylvain practice, 22
prostitution
Goldfield, 22
prostitution, Block 16, Hoover Dam,
73
Puleo, Lisa
exec. direct. Clark Co. Med. Soc.,
xi

Q

Quagliana, Dr. Joseph
bio., 185
oncologist, 141
Quebec, Canada, 10
Quimby, Margaret
George daughter, 87
Quinn, Dr. Edward, 149
bio., 185

R

Raines, Tom
UMC Found., 145
Ravenholt, Dr. Otto, 73
bio., 178
Clark Co. health officer, 35
Ray, Dixie Lee
DOE, 154
Reals, Dr. William, 117
bio., 182
Regan, Janie
Barger wife, 95, 99

Reid, Senator Harry, 148
jobs for workers at test site, 164
Reno
1940 population, 2
Reynolds Elect. & Eng. Co.
(REECO), 138, 156
Richardson, Bill
DOE (sec.), 154
Riesz, George
UMC adm., 144
Ririe, Dr. William B.
bio., 179
Ely, 27
Roantree, Dr. Robert P.
bio., 179
Elko Clinic, 27
Robbins, Jill, 44. *See* Jill Starzynski
Rogers, Jim
Channel 3 TV, 146
Roosevelt, Pres. Franklin, 32
Rose de Lima Hosp., 41.
See Saint Rose de Lima Hosp.
Ruckward, William
Sylvain college friend, 12
Sylvain high school friend, 11
Sylvain hockey teammate, 13
Russell, Diane
Las Vegas Review, 43
Russell, Dr. Willis
Barger partner, 110, 111
bio., 183

S

Sahara Hotel, 29
Saint Mary's Hosp., Rochester, Minn.,
69, 97
Saint Rose de Lima Hosp., 65, 71
Saint Rose Dominican Hosp., 65, 66,
143.
See Saint Rose de Lima Hosp.
Sal Sagev Hotel, 63, 64
salvarsen
treatment for syphilis, 22
San Pedro, Los Angeles, & Salt Lake
Railroad, 1
Saranac Lake, NY

United Nations
  atomic testing ban, 158
Univ. Med. Center (UMC), 30, 123.
  See Clark Co. Gen. Hosp.
  Child. Miracle Network Telethon,
    123
Univ. Med. Center Found., 144
Univ. Nev. Las Vegas (UNLV)
  nursing, 82
Univ. Nev. School of Med.
  (UNSOM), 30
Univ. of Nev. (UNR), 20
U.S. Pub. Health Service, 25

V
Valder, Ann
  Review Journal & Las Vegas Sun,
    144
Valley Hosp., 42, 149.
  See No. Las Vegas Hosp.
  children services, 147
Varone, Marlene.
  See Marlene Sylvain
venereal disease, 73
Veterans Admin. Outpatient Center
  Saint Rose, 31

W
Walley, D'Anne.
  See D'Anne Sylvain
Wallin, Angie
  UMC Found., 145
Watkins, Admiral
  DOE head, 156
West. Md. Methodist College, 52
White, William W.
  Nev. Sanitary Engineer, 26
Wilkinson, Evelyn, xi
Wilkinson, Ralph, xi
Winne, Dr. Burchard A., 25
Winne, Dr. Burchard E., 25
Woodbury, Dr. Claire, 32, 36, 41, 44, 66
  bio., 180
  Las Vegas Hosp. & Clinic, 28
  Las Vegas Muni. GC, 68
  Nev. Bd. of Health, 35

Z
Zucker, Dr. Ruben, 142

LIBRARY OF CONGRESS CATALOGING-IN-PUBLICATION DATA

Blachley, Annie.
  Good medicine : four Las Vegas doctors and the golden age of medicine /
Annie Blachley.
    p. cm.
  Includes bibliographical references and index.
  ISBN 0-9649759-7-1
    1. Physicians—Nevada—Las Vegas—Biography. 2. Medicine—Nevada—
Las Vegas—History. I. Title.

R277.B56   1999
610'.92'2793135—dc21
  [B]   99-088657